"There is nothing [...] physical illness when doctors don't have answers and the odds are stacked against you. This is a fiercely inspiring journey of a mother and daughter that never give up. It's a powerful example for all of us."

"Lisa's book takes the reader on a journey of grit and resilience. Her determination to help her mother and the love that drives through her comes across in waves as she shares an often emotional, yet very inspiring story. If you need a true story to reignite or even spark the fire that is burning in your soul then this is a must read."

"Relentless is one of the most thrilling, heart-rending adventure stories I've ever read. Lisa Tamati is a ferociously talented runner who's conquered some of the most grueling challenges on earth, but nothing put her heart and stamina to the test like the day her mother collapsed. From that moment on, Lisa had to dig into every trick of the endurance athlete's trade in her race to keep this courageous and loving woman alive. Read Relentless, and like me you'll be enthralled by Lisa's tale, enchanted by her family, and inspired to be like Lisa."

"Lisa Tamati has forged a name for herself by completing in some of the worlds most gruelling races in extreme conditions. "I can't" simply does not exist in her vocabulary. When faced with the biggest challenge of her life, Lisa does what she knows how, and fights! This inspirational true story of love and commitment sheds light on the impossible being possible and gives us all hope, no matter, what health condition we face. A must read!"

Ben Warren,
Celebrity nutritionist, holistic health expert,
and founder of BePure

"Lisa Tamati has conquered the toughest distance runs in the world. She did not know the word 'impossible' until she decided to save her mother. With guts and love even she didn't know she had, she proved that impossible was not an option."

Kathrine Switzer,
Women's running revolutionary,
author of *Marathon Woman*, and founder of '261
Fearless'
And
Roger Robinson,
Champion runner, author of
***When Running Made History*, legendary historian**

"An inspiring story about hope, the human spirit, and refusing to accept that you are powerless. Full of lessons for us all."

Dr Paul Wood
Speaker, Author, Facilitator

"Even though the challenges we face may not be as obviously arduous as those faced by Lisa, we can all learn something from her courage, tenacity, and unrelenting love for her mother."

Te Radar
Comedian and TV personality

"What do you do when there seems like there's no hope? Well, Lisa Tamati and her family fought, and fought hard. When left with the prospect of losing their beloved Mum, Isobel, they battled to keep her alive, keep her home, and bring her back. This heartwarming story of the love of a family and what it takes to prevail over an avalanche of obstacles."

J. J. Virgin,
Four times New York Times bestselling author,
celebrity nutrition & fitness expert

"The bond between mother and child is unbreakable. Times of trials and tribulations bring unrelenting forces into a reality, and Lisa and her mother Isobel are both a testament to the word relentless, because love and an unshakable belief can bring us through the darkest of times. this book is a must read to understand that we are all capable of more than we think."

Josh Komen,
Author of *The Wind At My Back*,
two times Leukaemia survivor and elite athlete

"An incredible story of how the powerful bond between daughter and mother defies conventional medicine to achieve the most inspirational medical recovery. When a never say never attitude is combined with a fierce drive to explore all options, anything is possible."

Dr Nick Kimber, PhD
Personalised nutrition and health specialist,
and Director of Elevate Health

"A truly remarkable story about two remarkable women, Lisa Tamati has written a magnificent and heartfelt account of her battle to save her mother. It's not just about both these women's incredible strength and courage. It also tells us so much about the power of the human spirit to triumph over seemingly insurmountable odds, and inspires us to question and go beyond what we think – or are being told – is possible."

Matthew Wolf,
Hollywood actor and producer

"After an unexpected crisis, Lisa's total devotion and love for her mum, Isobel, is inspiring. This story is a must-read for anyone looking to overcome obstacles in a positive, uplifting way. I loved this book!"

Molly Sheridan,
Extreme endurance athlete, speaker, and
author of *Running Past Midnight*

"As someone who has come back from a major stroke this is the most valuable resource I have ever read! This book is heartwarming, vulnerable and courageously honest just like Lisa."

Mike King,
New Zealander of the Year, TV Personality, mental
health advocate

"Lisa is one of the most amazing and inspiring people I have ever met or interviewed. This story screams from the mountain tops to never ever give up. I share this story over and over again when I want patients to have motivation to stick to a program to try to get well on a very difficult healing journey. I would recommend this book to everyone in a body as we all will eventually face challenges we never dreamed of and we have to know how to dig deep to overcome them."

Dr. D. Lindsey Berkson,
Host of the Dr. Berkson's Best Health Radio Show,
author of many books such as *SEXY BRAIN*,
***Hormone Deception, Safe Hormones, Smart Women*,**
and the *Berkson Blog* as Dr LindseyBerkson.com

"Relentless is the perfect title for this fast paced, page turner. Like Lisa Tamati herself, the book never slows down and never stops charging forward. Some challenges in life are self inflicted and some are thrust upon us but Lisa approaches every challenge with equal gusto and determination. We can all learn something from Relentless and from Lisa herself. This story is raw and engaging from start to finish. It will speak to you long after you have finished reading it."

Charlie Engle,
Extreme Adventurer, star of the feature film
Running the Sahara*, and author of *Running Man

"Lisa revives the essence of what it is to show courage, grit and resilience in an ever increasing fragile world. This book is inspiration to us all on how to find our inner strength and know that we all have what it takes to get through life's difficulties."

Tom Cronin,
Producer and Co-Writer of *The Portal* Film and
Book

"A hero is someone that refuses to let anything stand in her way, and Lisa Tamati is such an individual. Faced with the insurmountable challenge of bringing her ailing mother back to health, Lisa harnessed a deeper strength to overcome impossible odds. Her story is gritty, genuine and raw, but ultimately uplifting and endearing. If you want to harness the power of hope and conviction to overcome the obstacles in your life, Lisa's inspiring story will show you the path."

Dean Karnazes,
NY Times best selling author, *Extreme Endurance*
Athlete

RELENTLESS

How a mother and daughter defied the odds

LISA TAMATI

Relentless: How a Mother and Daughter Defied the Odds
© Lisa Tamati 2020

ISBN: 978-1-925935-99-8 (Paperback)
          978-1-925935-98-1 (eBook)

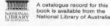 A catalogue record for this book is available from the National Library of Australia

Co-Author: Cushla Young
Lead Editor: Kristy Martin
Editors: Peta Culverhouse
Cover Image by: Stephanie Matuku
Cover Design: Ocean Reeve Publishing
Design and Typeset: yourbooks.co.nz
Printed by yourbooks.co.nz

Published by Lisa Tamati and Ocean Reeve Publishing
www.oceanreevepublishing.com

REEVE
PUBLISHING

Contents

Contents

*To my parents: you sacrificed so much for us,
my love for you both is as deep as the ocean.*

*To my brothers: through thick and thin we have
weathered the storms together, and are forever
bound by love.*

*To my husband: Haisley, you are my rock, my life,
my love.*

*To Cushla: I couldn't have finished this book without
your help.*

*To Kelli Culver and Neil Wagstaff: thank you for your
continued support.*

Introduction

The bond between a parent and their child is one of the strongest. When we dig deep into what binds us, we discover strength, resilience, and love. When this bond is threatened, we find out more about ourselves, what we are capable of, and what it means to overcome insurmountable odds. We find hidden strengths and discover reserves we never thought we had. This book is about an unbreakable bond between a mother and a daughter. It is about fierce hope and what it takes to beat the odds.

Relentless offers a blueprint for those going through their own tough times, trials, and tribulations. It presents a path to becoming stronger, wiser, and more resilient. It teaches that through adversity, we each have an opportunity to transform into a stronger, wiser person. It is about the recovery and the journey after a life-threatening event; about being open to stand up for a person's rights and about sacrifices that can bring about miracles. It also delivers some important messages and provides data and resources on recovery treatments that people need to be aware of, should they ever find themselves in a similar situation.

On January 24th 2016, my seventy-four year old mum, Isobel, was struck by an aneurysm – a massive gaping hole blew out in one of her arteries – blood and debris dispersed throughout her brain. As her life hung in the balance, a battle for that life raged for weeks. If I think back to that fateful day and dwell on the sudden grief and horror, the pain of it can almost crush me. Seeing her there so helpless in the days, weeks, and months that followed was one of the hardest moments of my life. Watching her hooked up to a dozen machines and tubes, my world burst apart. Nothing can prepare you for this moment.

The prognosis was bleak. From the first arrival in the hospital, she was ignored—that alone could have killed her—but she survived.

During the twelve hours it took to get her airlifted to Wellington Hospital, she could have died at any moment— but she survived.

For weeks, we didn't know whether she would live or in what state she would be in if she did— but she survived.

We were told if she did make it, she would be very unlikely to have any quality of life again— but she did.

After three months in hospital, we were told she wouldn't be with us long and that we should put her in a hospital care facility to see out her days in comfort. We don't do comfort, and we refused.

We were told after three months of rehab that she would likely never walk again— but she walked.

We were told after the toughest twelve months of rehab that her mental capacity was below the level of the lowest dementia patient; she is now a fully functioning, intelligent woman.

Three gruelling years later, Mum has her full driver's license back; she has her power of attorney and is fully capable of making her own decisions. She loves being at home and living independently. Mum is 90% healed and getting stronger every day. She is so happy and grateful that we never gave up.

Through this horrific journey, I resolutely believed I would get her back. I was determined to prove them all wrong. Mum is the centre of our family's world.

I believed that we could turn this tragedy into one of the greatest comeback stories of all time. We did. I believed we could turn this journey into one of the greatest learning times in our lives; that we could find blessings amongst the chaos; that we would bond together as a family; that we would gain positive new perspectives on life, and that we would use this to empower and encourage others. This book is the culmination of all of this. There is a reason for every hard and frightening and terrible thing you go through; it's up to you to find the positive in it.

So, if you love a story that has a happy ending, that empowers and enlightens, then read on.

Throughout the text, there are accompanying video clips that tell the story better than words ever could. They are an integral part of the story. These can be found at lisatamati.com/playlist or by simply hovering your phone over the QR code below using the camera function, and following the prompts to the website.

You will also find some other resources around mindset, health, and motivation that I hope will help you on your journey. These resources are free.

In addition to these, this book also tells the stories behind some of the races in my 25 year-long ultramarathon running career. You can view five of my many documentaries including the Gobi Desert 250km, Death Valley 217km, the Indian Himalayas 222km, Run the Planet in outback Australia 140km, Mt Manaslu – Nepal 212km for free by visiting: https://lisatamati. rocketspark.co.nz/page/playlist/

Chapter One
Our World Crumbles

'Mum's collapsed and she's in terrible pain. Get over here now!' I'll remember those words forever etched into my memory. It was the end of life as we knew it, and the start of a very different one.

***

I heard the phone ringing from the lounge, but rolled over and ignored it, just letting it ring out as I lay there enjoying the warmth beneath the covers. Then it rang again, and my mind began to click into gear. You know when you're struggling toward full consciousness, when you're not quite there but that horrible thought jumps into your mind: *Why is someone so desperate to get a hold of me so early in the morning?*

As the phone kept echoing down the hall, I threw off the covers and stumbled out of bed. Something was wrong, I could feel it in my gut. I ran to the lounge, and when I heard my brother's voice through the phone, I suddenly felt sick with fear.

'Mum's collapsed and she's screaming in pain. I have rung the ambulance. Get over here!'

He didn't say much more than that; he didn't need to. I knew from the panic in his voice that it was bad. I hung up and yelled at my partner as I rushed around, trying to pull my thoughts into a semblance of order. I must have been panicking, because I could hear Haisley telling me to calm down. My partner is always the calm, collected one.

Calm down! I thought, as I hurried about, grabbing anything I might need. *How can I calm down? Mum is my world. She is the rock that has saved me through so many storms in my life. How can anything bad happen to my precious mum? Please God, not my mum.*

My head was everywhere—my thoughts were racing from one thing to the next. You know, the way your mind goes into overdrive when you're only given one tiny piece of information? It leaves you guessing about all the worst of possibilities. I scrambled into a dress as we raced out the door. My husband jumped into the driver's seat, knowing I was in no fit state to drive. As soon as we pulled into Mum and Dad's driveway, I jumped from the car and ran through the front door.

'What happened?' I called out.

My brother, Dawson, answered, 'She's gone to hospital. The ambulance has taken her and said something about a possible stroke or something. She woke up early with a headache and collapsed on the bathroom floor.'

It felt like the ground had dropped out from under my feet. My mind raced, thinking through all the reasons she could have collapsed. None of them were good. Dawson kept talking,

'I was getting ready to go out for a morning surf when Dad came over and said, "Might want to come and check on your mother".'

Might want to check on her! Like it was no big deal that his wife had collapsed on the bathroom floor! I couldn't understand how Dad was so calm. He is the kind of person who doesn't like to make a fuss, and he does play things down out of habit. Both my parents are like that really; they're the type who don't make a fuss. I now wonder was he calm, or in shock, or did he just not realise the gravity of the situation?

Dad had been a fireman, so he'd seen it all: house-fires, car crashes, terrifying situations, the works. So maybe that was why he seemed so in control? I knew Mum wouldn't complain unless something was very wrong. She was tough like that. Never once complaining about being sick, or sore, or tired. She just got on with it, always looking out for other people and making sure they were alright. I actually think she'd die quietly just so she didn't make a fuss.

I was in full panic mode. You spend a lot of time in your own head as an athlete, battling yourself and your own demons, but when it's about your family, or your mum for that matter, it's something else. I was totally unprepared for something as close to home as this. A very different challenge lay ahead that my particular brand of mental toughness wasn't fully prepared for. I remember thinking about something Dad had said about his years working as a fireman: 'Whenever a crisis happens, you're never going to help anyone if you run around like a headless chook. Control yourself.'

At that moment, I understood what he meant. I needed to assess the situation as best I could and take action. I had to put everything aside—my worries—and concentrate on what had to be done right now. I had to focus on what was logical. I decided I had better get my shit together.

I started packing a set of clothes for Mum and told my brothers we would meet them at the hospital. I remember so vividly moving around the house, getting ready to be at the hospital as soon as possible, when I stopped to see Dad just standing off to the side, puffing on a cigarette. He looked at me and said, 'She'll be alright.'

I opened my mouth to respond but I couldn't think of anything to say because I still couldn't decide if Dad was just keeping himself under control or if he was in shock. What was I supposed to say to that? Would she be alright? I didn't even know what the problem was.

Haisley took me up to the hospital. I spent the car ride berating myself for not checking on Mum the night before. I'd been in the area, on the way back from surfing down the coast, and even though I could have checked on her, I didn't. When a massive tragedy happens in your life, you start to look back and think about all the things you've done wrong, and what you could have done differently. How you wouldn't have said *that*, or you would have done *this* instead. Or even how you could have told them you loved them just one more time. Hindsight's a bitch like that, and I'd soon learn there'd be a lot of moments like that in the days, weeks, months, and even years to come.

Chapter Two
Isobel

My mum was a wartime baby, born in 1941 in New Plymouth, New Zealand. She was conceived while her dad was home on leave. When he returned home from fighting, he was met with a three-year old, slightly precocious daughter, Isobel. Given his absence, Mum had a close relationship with her own mother that continued through into adulthood. Her sister, Peggy, was born when she turned eight. Mum immediately fulfilled the role as second mother looking after her sister, and this formed her nurturing temperament from a young age. Her brother, Grant, was born when Mum was fourteen. When Grant turned fourteen, they lost their dad. He passed away of an aneurysm aged only fifty-three, leaving a young Grant without a father figure. My mum had already met my dad at this point, so they had a lot to do with Grant's upbringing. Family was the most important thing in the world to Isobel. She made a lot of sacrifices for her family growing up and then again when we arrived.

Despite being determined and intelligent, Isobel struggled at school. She had dyslexia, which was only acknowledged in 2007 as a legitimate disability by the

New Zealand Ministry of Education. She tells stories of getting the strap when she got her spelling wrong. The system fed back to her that she wasn't very bright. One day, when she came home from school with her report card, her Dad said to her, 'Oh well dear, at least you'll be good with your hands like me.' He too was dyslexic and had made a career as a builder. It was expected that Isobel would settle into being a housewife and that would be her lot. Wanting to prove everyone wrong and fuelled by her desire to become a teacher, she went to Teachers College.

Isobel met my dad, Cyril, the summer between high school and college. It was New Year's Eve. Both my parents attended a local dance, each with a different date. It was one of those, *I saw you across the dance floor* moments. A kiss under the trees at Burgess Park that night was the beginning of a fifty-year relationship. They didn't marry straight away and a long distance courtship began. Isobel completed her teacher's training and then travelled to Australia with some girlfriends. After being away from Dad for eight months or so, he called and asked her to come home. They were engaged and lived separately in Wanganui for a few years while Mum taught at Brunswick School. It was the early 1960s and being that Dad was Māori and Mum was Pākehā, they received quite a bit of flack for being in a mixed-race relationship. However, they managed to fight through all the hurdles society had to throw at them, and in 1965, after a five-year courtship, they married and then went back to live in New Plymouth. Mum taught at Fitzroy School, until I was born in 1968.

I was followed by my brother, Dawson, two-and-a-half years later, and then Mitchell, eighteen months after that. Growing up in New Plymouth was fabulous. With Mount Taranaki and the beaches so close, we were typical children of the 1970s. We would leave the house straight after school to play in the streets or at the beach with other kids and return home when it got dark or when we became hungry. I always tried to keep up with my brothers. I was a feisty sister—bossy to the core—but always wanting to keep up with the boys and, more importantly, Dad and his mates. Whatever they did, I wanted to do it too, which presented no problems pre-puberty but was a battle afterwards. They didn't necessarily want their sister chasing them around all the time. Dad had high expectations of us, particularly when it came to sport. He desperately wanted all of us to represent New Zealand. As a child, the pressure was often immense.

When we began school, Mum became a teacher's aide so she could be at the same school as her children. She virtually sacrificed her career to be close to us, and her life centred around us which we—as egocentric littlies—just expected. *Isn't that normal?* Dad's twenty-four-hour shifts at the fire station meant Mum was alone with us a lot. When Dad was home, Mum would make sure that we didn't wake him up or cause trouble. Dad had a lot on his plate and needed his time out, so Mum played peacemaker. She kept it all together and was the centre of our worlds.

Mum had a real compassion for students who struggled, either through dyslexia, disability, or trauma. Not only did she nurture us, but over the next few

decades Isobel helped hundreds of people. She became
an adult literacy teacher and tutored young adults,
enabling them to turn their lives around. There were
many occasions when we would get home and a stray
kid would be at our table. She was forever opening our
house up to those who were lost, broken, or needing
some love. She would patch them up, feed them, and
send them on their way. There have been dozens of times
when I have been walking down the street with Mum
and someone has stopped us to say, 'Isobel, you had a
massive impact on my life. I might not have come back
after class to say thank you, so I want you to know how
you empowered me. I now know who I am ...'

I've heard similar versions of this story so many times.
Some of these characters would be seen as dangerous;
they may have just got out of prison. But Isobel had
love for them all. She accepted who they were and where
they had come from. She didn't put up with much shit
from anyone, but she became the mother figure that
they needed.

As we grew up, we each flew the nest. Dawson left to
follow a professional rugby career in Wales and England.
Mitchel travelled all over the world for years. I left home
in my early twenties for Europe, mostly living in Austria
over the next decade and a half. However, the call to
home was strong.

Each of us now live back in New Plymouth. We're
kept here by the love of the outdoors, family, and the
surf. Both of my brothers have spent half their lives in
the ocean. So, despite living away from home in our
twenties and thirties, we remained a close-knit family
with strongly embedded family values.

Mum passed on her fierce determination and stubbornness—some would say—to me. At the age of twenty-nine and having already completed a few epic adventures during my travels, I found the ultra-marathon world. My introduction into this tribe was the Marathon Des Sables. Imagine being surrounded by seven hundred marathon runners in the middle of the Sahara Desert, about to run 242km in a six-day multi-stage race? I had no idea that this event would catapult me into a world that would consume my life over the next twenty years. The run was hard, don't get me wrong, but I was hooked. During those few days of adventure, sweat and tears, I rediscovered who I really was. The ultra-marathon community is one of the most supportive and affirming sports groups that one could belong to. With my newfound self-esteem, I went on to run approximately 140 ultra runs.

I followed the Marathon Des Sables with another super race, the Desert Cup: a 168km non-stop run through Jordan. In contrast to the Marathon Des Sables, where a mighty camp travels along with the runners, stopping every night for a sleep and refuelling, the Desert Cup only had checkpoints every 25- 30km. Here, runners could fill up for water. Most of the time you were on your own. And did I mention there were wild dogs too? At one point in the middle of the night, I was lost, had run out of water and was surrounded by these nasty creatures. I was terrified and so relieved when I eventually found the next checkpoint. Next-level scary! This run took me around forty-six hours to complete and was a very big step up on the previous ultramarathons. But even though it was brutal, this race only fuelled my obsession. From here on, I would run six-hour, ten-hour, twelve-hour, and twenty-four-hour races; mountain ultras, marathons, 80km and 100km races; basically, everything I could find. I would use smaller ultras as preparation for longer ones. One of the hardest ones I did, as far as the legs went, was along the Isar River in Germany, running 338km in five days. Around 70km a day put me on crutches for three weeks. I thought this was the end of my career. The pain and swelling in my legs during that event was beyond imagining but my mind got me through.

I was living with my then husband, Gerhard. Over this thirteen-year period of my life, Mum would travel to Europe to see me. Inevitably while she was there, I had some race I was either preparing for or running in. Mum would join me, driving alongside me as I trained. We would often make a weekend of a race, allowing Mum and I to enjoy exploring together in whatever country the race was in. Mum could tell that I was getting a lot out of running ultras and so she supported me as I entered run after run, but she still retained her motherly concern for her daughter. I missed her greatly when she would return to New Zealand after these trips, and I would pine for my home for weeks after.

While back at home in New Zealand, Mum and Dad cheered me on and often worried about what I was up to next. The race that really scared me was a 333km run through the Niger, which at the time was the second poorest country on earth. I had been training for over a year for it with my husband. We were meant to run it together, as this was race was really hard. But one week out from the run, and completely out of the blue, Gerhard told me he wanted a divorce. I was devastated and shell-shocked. It had hit me hard and with no forewarning, I was reeling from this. We had been together for six years, and I couldn't believe he would do this to me right now, a week from what would be one of the hardest races I would ever run. Going into this race, my head just wasn't in the game. Perhaps any sane person would have pulled the pin. But there was a part of me that knew that quitting now wasn't an option I was prepared to live with. When I set out to do something, I don't change course easily, despite the chaos that was about to rip through my life, my career, and my financial security. I would soon lose everything, but I had worked so hard to organise and train for this event and had sponsors and a film crew that I was very much obliged to go through with it. I pulled myself together as best I could and soldiered on, but my heart was breaking.

The Niger race was horrifically organised. There were only seventeen runners entered. In all the races I had done previously, there were usually 200-700 runners and the organisation was top notch. This was a completely different ball game. As we landed at the airstrip, I looked out the window to see an upturned, crashed aircraft on the runway, left there to rust. Next to me aid workers were wearing the Red Cross emblem on their shirts. This was not your usual tourist destination. Large men carrying AK-47 assault rifles met us on the airstrip, and I started to think that perhaps I should have given this run a miss. Everything was terrifying and my head and heart were breaking. As we left the airport, the first thing I saw was the beggars, the victims of leprosy, and the chaos of the unpaved roads.

The race director was an ex-French Foreign Legion man, a hard ass if ever there was one. He was someone more interested in the money than anything else, which we came to realise pretty quickly. He had organised for food to arrive from France to be available at the checkpoints, but the food was nowhere to be seen. No doubt hijacked by some corrupt official.

The next morning, we hopped into a convoy of vehicles and headed into the desert. We drove two days to the start line, going deep in the depths of the Niger Sahara. Our meagre food supplies now consisted of a stinking dead goat attached to the roof of one of the four-wheel drives and cans of mushy peas. This was to nourish us over the next six or so days.

Everything about this run was just wrong and crazy. We had naively expected it to be something it wasn't, and we were quite deep in the proverbial, with no way out but through. The tension between my still-then husband and I was palpable, and to be honest I was scared out of my wits. Never had I signed up to run this one alone; the plan had been to do it together, watching out for and supporting each other. That was now gone, and I was facing this most dangerous and scary challenge: running 333km across this very dangerous and politically unstable part of the Sahara.

And then, as we were just starting the race, the inevitable happened. One hour into the race the food poisoning struck. The goat stew I had eaten the night before was coming back to bite me on the ass. That whole day and into the night was horrific: vomiting, dysentery, blood sugar problems, massive dehydration issues, all while staring down the barrel of a 333km run.

I was sick—very sick. By the time the night had arrived, I was fainting and collapsing, alone and frightened. At one point, as I lay unconscious in the sand, one of the other runners—a girl from England called Ellie—found me and stayed with me. She got my sleeping bag out and tried to warm me up in order to wake me up. She got fluid into me after a while. She was amazing, and I was so grateful. Ellie helped me up and tried to keep me upright as we limped slowly toward checkpoint one.

Again and again, I collapsed, until two more runners found us and helped us limp into the checkpoint. Once more, I considered pulling out of the race. While being treated by the race doctor, one of the other runners, who had also ingested the goat stew, said he was also in dire straits. He suggested we run together to the next checkpoint. Again, I was so grateful to have another supportive runner by my side, we pooped our way along the next section of the run, stopping every ten minutes to get rid of that goat from our system, from whichever end it decided to come. I had no dignity left after the first hour.

Added to this, there were other dangers around. At the time, there was a civil war going on between the locals and the military protecting the Chinese oil and gas companies conducting explorations. Corruption ran high in this land, and the locals would never see any of the spoils.

As we ran, we saw a massive dust cloud off in the distance, getting closer and closer. A convoy of oil exploration vehicles and military protection vehicles thundered their way across the desert sands. We were scared stupid and did our best to get out of the way, as far as possible, to avoid the heavily armoured trucks. But it was hard to know where they were heading, and we couldn't go far off course. They motored past us without even slowing down—it was a frightening sight.

During another section of the race, when I was running on my own again, a large salt caravan (truck) pulled up alongside me stacked high with salt, other items, and over a hundred Tuareg men in the back. Here I am: a woman, on her own, in the desert looking pretty vulnerable. I thought, *Fuck! This is it!*

'Where the hell are you going? You're going to die!' Asked the driver in French as he pulled up beside me.

'I'm in a race going to Agadez,' I yelled in my non-existent French, as I pointed forwards. Agadez was still hundreds of kilometres away.

'Get in the truck! You will die out here!'

'Nah, it's all good thanks.' I was terrified and thinking to myself: *Just when you thought it couldn't get any worse. A broken heart, a pending divorce, trying to run 333 km across the Sahara with food poisoning, and now this!*

Realising that I wasn't about to accept their help, they left me, shaking their heads. It seems that they were just being nice but again that could have gone very differently. Someone was watching over me still.

I survived this race somehow, but it was the probably the worst sixty-six hours of my life.

There was another adventure that was comparable: the Libyan Desert Expedition, an illegal 250km unsupported expedition through a military barred zone with only two litres of water a day; the full story of which is detailed in my book: *Running Hot*[1].

---

[1] Tamati, Lisa. (2009) *Running Hot*. Auckland: Allen & Unwin.

I then had to return to Austria—a failure in the race and in life. I had to pack up what little I had. I lost the house, the car, the business, and even the country I was living in, not to mention my husband. At thirty-eight years old, I came home to Mum and Dad, broken. It would take me years to properly get back on my feet, financially, mentally, and physically. But running would again be the catalyst in rebuilding my mind and my confidence. It was the only thing that kept me sane during these tough times. It helped rebuild my world, and it was at this point that I managed to qualify for a race I had wanted to do for over a decade: the Badwater Ultra Marathon, a 217km run through the hottest desert on earth—Death Valley, California—and the unofficial world championships of our sport.

This was the big league and right now, at a time when I really needed something positive to fight towards, this became my new focus. It was one hell of a campaign to pull together, costing over $50 000.00 in sponsorship money. The logistics of crew, and a film team from *20/20* made this an all-consuming project, but one that absolutely changed the course of my career. I went over there, and it was life changing. I was strong, had the most amazing crew anyone could wish for, and smashed it. The documentary and ensuing book and sponsorship deals helped me get back up on my feet, well, at least to some degree. I just hustled my way forward, ending up with some major sponsorship deals, another Death Valley run the following year and much more.

Playlist Link: Death Valley-Running The Badwater ultramarathon at lisatamati.com/Playlist.

Meanwhile, Mum was diligently crewing for me again for my many events. She was also holding the fort for me at the jewellery shop that her and I built from scratch. I was gone, either training or racing, and she was always consistently my support.

Mum also crewed for me in several twenty-four hour races in Auckland, where she would stay up all night and make sure I was still holding it all together. One of these twenty-four hour races, which happened to be the New Zealand Nationals, I finally ended up achieving a new record: 194.3km in twenty-four hours. I had attempted it seven times prior and failed the 185km cut off every time, so finally a few things were going my way.

For years, I tried in gymnastics, later surfing, and now in ultramarathoning to represent my country, something that my dad had told us he expected of us since we were littlies. Damn it felt good, at age forty-one, to go back home to Dad and hand him my shirt with the silver fern on it. I said, in a loving way, 'There you go you old bastard. Don't tell me ever again that I don't finish what I start,' something he had always said I did.

He replied, 'Well, it's about bloody time. It only took you twenty-five years longer than I had planned, but well done.' He is a hard man to please.

This was a dream I had held since I was five years old. I got to go to the Commonwealth Championships and proudly smash out another twenty-four hours with that bloody silver fern on my shirt. Epic days. Dreams do come true.

Later on, I would also come up with the crazy idea to run the length of New Zealand for charity. Again,

Mum would be there by my side during hours of training. For the entire run, she drove the follow car, all 2,250km and forty-two days of it. Can you imagine driving 9-10 km per hour, for forty-two days and then having a shitty, absolutely knackered daughter to deal with at night? Legend.

Throughout her life, Mum was a ferocious carer of others; she put everyone else before herself. But this would ultimately cause us to be in the situation we were in now. With aneurysms in the family history, being pre-diabetic and struggling with her weight, we didn't realise that our strong and determined mum would suddenly be as helpless as a baby, but here we were. The role reversal of mother and daughter was absolute. As a family, we would spend over three years building mum back to as close as possible to the person that she was before.

Chapter Three
A Medical Disaster

When we arrived at the Taranaki Base Hospital, Mum was writhing in pain in one of the emergency room open cubicles. She was holding her head in a desperate state, in agony. The shock of seeing her like that was a blow that hit me square in the chest. I just knew it had to be bad. The hospital staff told us they thought she had a migraine, and that they'd given her some painkillers to ease the pain. But as I looked down at Mum, I knew it was more than that. I knew she wouldn't be moaning like that with *just* a migraine. I say, "just" because she had suffered from them before. When she was younger, migraines were something she thought would just be a part of her everyday life. She suffered from them terribly for over fifteen years and just fought on when she had one. She had tried many different cures. Since going gluten free she hadn't experienced a migraine in over twenty years. And even when she was ill with something, she would just quietly take herself off to bed. She wasn't a drama queen. This definitely wasn't a migraine, but the doctor wasn't having a bar of it.

As we waited for the painkillers to set in, I tried to comfort Mum as best I could. I reached out to hold her hand, just hoping to lend her some of my strength as she slipped further away from us. I looked at the heart monitor and blood pressure machine so many times, just watching the beeping line go up and down, and the numbers on the screen changing, just wishing I could do something. I felt so powerless, unable to do anything to help her. She was my mum; this beautiful, powerful woman that had spent her entire life helping people, and I couldn't do anything to help her when she needed me the most. That waiting. That was the worst part, just sitting there watching the hospital move around us as time ticked by; Mum got worse and everyone just ignored us.

It's such a life-changing moment when something horrific happens to a parent. They give birth to you and raise you, and are always the strong ones, in control. They're the ones who look after you when you're sick. To see Mum in that state was a strange role-reversal, and I had no idea how far that reversal would go in the months and years to come. I had a sudden and sickening feeling: I had reached that age where parents died. Seeing my Mum so vulnerable made me feel old. I had always been a mummy's girl, and Mum had gone above and beyond, always helping, loving unconditionally, and supporting me through all the crap I had been through growing up. Now I felt like the rug had been pulled from under my feet: my rock, my safe place, my protector now needed me to be hers. It struck me hard, and I remember asking myself, *How the hell did we both get this old? What happened? Where did the time go? I am not ready for this stage of life.* The panic that I was trying desperately to control rose up, again and again, as I watched her, *Not yet! I'm not ready yet!*

We spent about six hours just waiting around her bed as this doctor decided what to do, if anything at all. Taranaki Base Hospital is a regional hospital, and for more serious injuries or illnesses patients are likely to be transferred to one of the main centres, all of which are a three to five hour drive away.

The doctor kept coming back to the migraines, which was a complete red herring.

When the ambulance originally took Mum to the hospital, the paramedic said that he thought she was having a stroke. He said it was either a Transient Ischaemic Attack (TIA) or a Cerebrovascular Accident (CVA). For all those out there who don't understand the lingo, a TIA is where the blood supply to your brain is temporarily blocked. After a TIA your risk of stroke is higher, and it can even be a warning that a stroke is on the way. A CVA is the medical term for a stroke. For whatever reason, the doctor ignored the paramedic. I wasn't there when the ambulance arrived at the hospital, so I didn't know this at the time. I found out after talking to the paramedic a year later. Whatever the case, because the doctor disagreed or just ignored the paramedic, we were left waiting for the painkillers to kick in.

Doctors are very busy and under a huge amount of stress, and they don't know your loved ones like you do. They don't know if your mother, brother, aunty, or cousin is acting strangely. There's an expectation that doctors know what they're talking about. We tend to sit back and let them do their job. But after a few horrifying experiences on this journey, I realised that was flawed thinking. The reality is doctors are human beings, who have a lot on their plates: patients, long hours, budget constraints, and stress. And human beings make mistakes. Doctors are trained in a very regimented way that sometimes doesn't allow for out-of-the-box thinking. I will always feel guilty for not saying more when I was just being too damned polite. But you don't know what you don't know. Although I regret not saying what I was thinking to the medical staff then – with a hell of a lot more force and assertiveness – I now make sure I communicate very clearly. It's important to trust your gut, follow your instincts. Double check everything and get second opinions. Do your own research and take some responsibility. Patients need advocates, and their families know them best.

After sitting in the hospital with Mum for six hours, I was getting desperate. No one was listening to us, and Mum was getting worse. She was still in excruciating pain. Suddenly, I had a brainwave. *Why hadn't I thought of it before? Megan Stewart!* She was a paramedic friend of mine who I knew was only too familiar with the medical system at Taranaki Base Hospital. If there was anyone who could get our point across or get us the help we needed, it would be her. I phoned and begged for help.

Megan and I have a long and rich history together. She's an ultramarathon running friend who'd also crewed for me on several of my big events and expeditions. We've always had a close and powerful bond, honed from doing crazy, extreme things in strange parts of the world together. I believe there's something to be said of friends who go through life changing things together;

the bonds just go way deeper than the usual superficial relationships we often have in our everyday lives.

Over the phone, I explained to Megan what had happened. I told her how Mum collapsed; that we were in the hospital; that she was in extreme pain, and she seemed to be slipping away from us. Megan knew what Mum was like – the type of woman who never complained about anything – so straight away, she knew something was wrong. It didn't take her long to get to the hospital. She walked in and, after hearing our story, took one look at Mum and said it was a stroke or aneurysm, or something major in her brain. It most certainly wasn't a migraine.

'I know this woman,' Megan cornered the arrogant doctor who had been fobbing us off for hours. 'This is not normal for her, and these symptoms are closer to serious brain injury, not a migraine. She might be having a stroke. You need to get her a CT scan, now.' Megan is a very strong, powerful, don't-mess-with-me kind of woman who runs deserts for fun, and does Jiu Jitsu for kicks and who is the "winch wench" (her words, not mine) on the Helicopter Rescue Team – the ones who risk their lives dangling from helicopters to save people. She knows her stuff, and her assertiveness paid off, because within half an hour Mum was taken in for a CT scan.

It took another hour of dreadful waiting before the scan results came back, and when they did all hell broke loose. Suddenly, the doctor finally decided to pay attention to what we were saying. She'd suffered a massive aneurysm: a rupture in one of the blood vessels in her brain, and her skull was filling up with blood. It was a huge aneurysm, and it was still bleeding. The words out the doctor's mouth resonate in my head still today: 'Her skull is filled with blood, and it's right throughout her brain.'

I looked at Megan, and I'll never forget the look in her eyes. All I could see was the fear, and I knew she was thinking that Mum wasn't going to survive.

This Emergency Doctor treated Mum like a neurotic old woman. His behaviour, in my opinion, was negligent. Unbeknown to us, Mum had another bleed under his supervision about four-to-six hours in. If she'd had a CT scan earlier, this would have been picked up. We would have been transferred to Wellington Hospital much sooner and the damage could have been vastly mitigated. In the days, weeks, and months ahead, I had always intended on filing an official complaint with the hospital, but I was too busy fighting for Mum's life. I was using every ounce of my being on just keeping Mum alive, and this is often the case with medical blunders: no one reports anything because they are too busy with the massive challenges at hand. As an addendum, I have heard second-hand that the doctor who was treating Mum was taken out of ED, with disciplinary proceedings undertaken; there were other cases where similar mistakes had occurred. If it had been up to me, he would have had more than that taken away from him.

The hospital staff started organising for an air ambulance to retrieve her and take her down to the Wellington Hospital—a large city hospital five hours drive away—where they had a dedicated Neurological Department. Nothing could be done in our local hospital. They had no facilities or staff for such events.

During this time, my family was in shock, not knowing what this all meant, but realising that it was dire and her life was hanging in the balance. It was amongst all that racing around that Dad spoke up, 'Well, we better start planning her funeral.'

For fifty-five years my parents have lived together as husband and wife. Mum is his world, but he was always a bit rough around the edges. He's the type of guy that doesn't indulge in emotions, and his pragmatism in this situation was dampening the shocking reality of our situation. I know it was just Dad's way of coping and, in that moment, I did what others had done for me when I was broken. I held my seventy-six year old father around the shoulders and said gently, 'Dad, as long as she is still breathing, we are going to fight for her. I will move heaven and earth to get her back to us. Just follow me and do everything I need you to, okay?'

I wasn't sure what I was going to do if Mum didn't survive, but I couldn't let myself even consider that option right now. I've heard it said that great leaders pretend a situation isn't as bad as it is, and then proceed to make it better than it is. I decided to try and do exactly that.

My dad, ever the trooper, said, 'Right, what do you need me to do?' I knew from the strife I had been in during expeditions and races that when people are in crisis, giving them tasks stops their brains going off the deep end; the action of having something to do produces some sort of feeling of control. In a situation like this, that was what my entire family needed. I started giving out jobs. I knew how bad the situation was, and I knew that to get through it we were going to have to put one foot in front of the other. We had to begin to compartmentalise and quell the panic. I'd spent thousands of kilometres with nothing other than the demons in my mind, and I knew how to hold them down temporarily. I knew we'd have to stay strong for each other, so as the doctors prepared to airlift Mum to Wellington Hospital, I mentally shifted into operational mode.

I started organising my brothers, my father, and our extended family. I put plans into motion and had everyone moving to meet in Wellington. *Do this. Collect that. Don't forget this.* It was good for me to be doing something, so I didn't have time to stop and think about what was happening. Meanwhile, Mum kept getting bumped down the priority list for transfer. Because of her age, the air ambulance kept putting others ahead of her, even though we were told she could die at any moment.

I look back in horror at the length of time my Mum endured all that pain, and the time it took to get any type of help. It is said that speed is critical in an event like this. Getting the patient into surgery within the first sixty minutes is the "gold standard." They often say that it's the first ninety minutes that are the most critical to a patient's survival; but Mum waited *eighteen hours*. Eighteen hours of further damage. One of the disadvantages of living in the provinces is that local hospitals often don't have the facilities for such cases. Knowing what I know now, I am amazed she survived that first day. And I am so glad I didn't know the implications of all of this then.

I don't spend a lot of time overthinking things before I do them: I just make decisions, take action, and figure it out as I go. For me to just sit there, unable to help Mum—who was in dire need of help—was probably one of the worst experiences of my life, if not *the* worst. This flimsy sense of control that we think we have just seemed to slip away. What you're left with is a feeling of loneliness and hopelessness. I knew in my bones that she was in big trouble, but I didn't know what to ask for. It was terrifying.

The whole time I had been waiting for the air ambulance, no one could tell me whether I would be allowed to travel with her. I can tell you there was no way I was leaving her side if I could help it. It felt like nothing could happen fast enough. The whole day felt as if everyone was moving in slow motion whilst Mum lay dying. The skull cavity is a fixed size, so when blood leaks out of blood vessels it fills an already full space. It squeezes and puts pressure on the brain and causes unimaginable pain and brain damage. Basically, her brain was dying with every passing minute. By the time the air ambulance crew finally arrived for the hand over, I was absolutely desperate. They were efficient, but time was ticking by. As I looked down at Mum's unconscious face, I kept thinking, *Hang in there, Mum*.

Chapter Four
Wellington Hospital where Reality Hits Hard

& Mum Marriage Worries

In the days leading up to Mum's aneurysm, life was busy as usual. We all had our own lives, and we were all doing our own thing. There had been a few warning signs. Mum had complained about a strong headache she'd been experiencing. She said it felt out of the ordinary, sitting just behind her left eye. With her history of migraines, I thought she must have eaten something with gluten in it. I wasn't worried when I booked her into the local General Practitioner (GP) for a check-up.

I know I couldn't have known what was going on, and I know the doctors can't be expected to send every person complaining of a headache to get a CT scan. But looking back, I just wish I had gone. That prick called hindsight rears his ugly head again. It all seems so obvious in the aftermath. The GP, unfortunately, was new to Mum. There was no real doctor-patient history. He thought she just had a stiff neck and instructed her to get a massage to ease the tension. When Mum complained of the same pain a day or two later, she knew it was something else. She went to the GP again, which was very unlike Mum. But again, he told her to keep working on releasing stress from her neck and the headaches should go.

I had always harboured this worry that she'd have a stroke or heart attack because of her weight, which she had always struggled to maintain. Her genetic make-up was such that she could train hard all day, eat a lettuce leaf, and still put on weight. Even after the aneurysm, when she was fed through a tube and was only ingesting small amounts per day, it took eighteen months for her to lose weight and even then she only lost 28 kg. It's just her genetic makeup, and problems with her metabolism and thyroid exacerbated that.

When I spoke to the same GP recently, he was devastated that he didn't pick up the aneurysm. I don't blame him at all for what happened, and I think this is an important lesson: you can't focus on your mistakes. Stuff happens in life and sometimes you just do the best you can to survive what is thrown at you. Sometimes we're all just coping in the best way we can, so it's important to not focus on the mistake, but instead think about the lesson.

Recently, I became involved in epigenetic testing programmes whilst coaching athletes through our business, Running Hot Coaching. Epigenetic testing is a programme that investigates someone's genetic profile using algorithms and various measurements to give 10 000 data points that then give detailed information on just how the person's genes are expressing, and what they need to do to optimise their health, performance and fitness. It was created over fifteen years ago by an international team of doctors, researchers, and technology programmers. The platform is informed by evidence-based medical research. While learning about epigenetics, we discovered Mum's genetic makeup meant she had predispositions to cardiovascular disease, diabetes, weight issues, and thyroid issues. Mum has hardening of the arteries, cardiovascular problems, fatty liver, was overweight, her cholesterol was too high, and she had high blood pressure. The likelihood of some sort of cardiovascular event was high. I'd been on her back for years about exercise and her diet. And she did try; she ate very little, went to aqua-aerobics four times a week, walked, and went to gym twice a week, but I knew it wasn't enough. That's because she always put her family first. She was, and still is, always looking after someone else in the family or the community, making sure they have everything they need, and never taking time to look after herself. This is something I discuss a lot with my athletes: that prioritising training, fitness, and health isn't being selfish. It's like putting your oxygen mask on first when the pressure drops in a plane. You are told to do your own first, and then help the others because you are no good to anyone if you are unconscious. The same principle applies.

I learned a lot in that time about the medical world: how decisions are made, why they're made, and what factors contribute to the process of making them. On that very first day, when the doctors finally got the results back from the CT scan, and they knew she had to get to Wellington Hospital if she was to survive, it wasn't as simple as just going. There was a long-winded process involved. She had to be prepped for the air ambulance and put on the waiting list. The team then had to fly up from Wellington and land at the airport, drive from the airport into Taranaki Base Hospital for the patient handover. Then, after her papers were reviewed, she would be driven to the airport, loaded onto the plane, and flown to Wellington. Only then could they prepare for the operation, and only then could she go into surgery. There are so many delays as procedures have to be followed. Also, you are prioritised according to a lot of factors, and one of them is age. At one point, we finally thought the air ambulance was coming, but a newborn baby somewhere had complications and we were bumped down the waitlist. You can't argue with that kind of logic, but when your family is involved, it's the worst feeling. When our time finally came, the team that arrived at the hospital displayed phenomenal service with their efficiency and professionalism. It's so fantastic that this service is available to us. How many lives have been saved due to the air ambulance service?

I didn't know too much about what was happening in those first hours and days. I didn't know the huge implications that an aneurysm bought with it. I later heard that when an aneurysm occurs, the pain is unimaginable. They call it a thunderclap headache because that's what it feels like: a storm in your head. My mum was so strong to deal with that sort of pain for so many hours.

We finally arrived in Wellington at 1:00am and the doctors quickly got her into surgery. We were told she had two aneurysms in her brain but only one of them had burst. However, that one was huge, at 16-18mm long. The size of it posed its own set of problems. At 3:00am, some twenty-one hours after this all began, Mum finally came out of the operating theatre. The surgeons had successfully inserted a shunt into her brain. She'd survived the initial surgery, and thankfully the bleeding had, at least for the moment, stopped. But we were still in dire straits because the aneurysm was still open, which meant it could start bleeding again at any moment.

Whilst Mum was in surgery, I'd been researching like crazy, trying to learn about the outcomes and possibilities for complications. Now, I know there are many critics of "Doctor Google." Some may roll their eyes when people search their symptoms before going to the doctor. There is a dark joke that an online diagnosis always ends up being cancer. However, never underestimate the power of the internet to give you information. Yes, there is a lot of rubbish you have to wade through, but if you sift through carefully and—most importantly—find out which sites to trust, the answers to pretty much everything is on there. You get access to the world's top doctors and scientists, leading edge research, studies, and much more. Besides, it was something to do while we waited. I wanted to load myself up on as many details as possible. It felt like the more knowledge I could gain, the higher the likelihood we had of stopping another balls-up like we had in the emergency department in New Plymouth, Taranaki Base Hospital.

As the days passed, I learned a critical factor about the brain and blood. Blood is toxic to the brain. When they mix, there is a possibility that vasospasms—spasms in part of the brain—can happen. Once I heard this word, I researched it and found out that this was going to be the major danger for Mum, going forward. Every time a vasospasm occurred, if they occurred (not everyone gets them), more of her brain could die. We could slowly lose

Mum, even though she had survived the initial episode. We learned there is a twenty-one day period after the aneurysm when these vasospasms can occur. Why exactly twenty-one days? I have no idea, but I learned that if she survived till then, she would probably have a good chance. So even though the drain had started to lower the pressure, and the bleeding had at least, for the moment, stopped, the chance of even more damage, or even death was critically high. More of her brain could die over the next three weeks. The doctors informed us we had two options for surgery, and both came with their own complications. It's horrible being put in that situation—having to make a decision that could change the outcome of your loved one's life forever or end it immediately.

Chapter Five
Two Options & Mum's Marriage Doubts

The odds were bad, really bad. There were two options:

Option 1: Major brain surgery. Chop through her skull to her brain and put a clasp in. 50% chance of dying right on the table. Now, when the doctors tell you that they want to cut your mother's head open your response is close to, *Fuck off! And option two is …?*

Option 2: Two operations. Going up through the femoral artery and putting a tiny platinum coil to seal off, so to speak, the open blood vessel in her brain. The hole was so big though that they could only "patch" up part of it with the coil and would have to do a second operation later, to get the other part done. They call this a Partial Coiling. There were no odds given for option 2, it was less risk but a high risk of causing another stroke.

The decision to go for Option 2—the partial coiling surgery—felt like a roll of the dice: we either had to commit to one big operation or two smaller ones. Once we had decided on the operation, it was time for Mum to be prepped for surgery. I remember trying desperately to hold it together as we hugged her and kissed her and told her how much we loved her. She seemed to comprehend what was going on. It was like that scene in the movies where they take your loved one away through those double doors. It was surreal. I felt like a child. It took everything not to run after her. It could be the last time I see her alive. I was sitting hard on all my emotions, trying to compartmentalise them as best I could, distracting myself with research and jobs to hold it together. Thankfully, my two cousins, Kim and Victoria Batchelor, who are like sisters to me, had flown in from Australia, and they were my strength.

The operation had many risks associated with it. We knew there was a chance of her having a stroke as the surgeons were operating in a tiny area and could accidentally block off other vessels. The wait while she was in the operating theatre was horrific. What the hell do you do with yourself? You pace the halls, trying not to imagine every possible scenario. I remember at one point that my younger brother, Mitchell, who is usually as a tough as nails, my Aunty Peg, and I were all bawling our eyes out, hugging each other. Mum was in such deep shit that we couldn't see a way out. The emotions came in waves. We were all scared out of our wits. We couldn't imagine carrying on without her. A world without her just didn't seem possible.

Finally, the wait was over, and Mum was bought back down to the neurological ward. The surgery was a semi success; the coiling had gone well. But it wasn't all good news. As the doctor explained, there were major implications from the surgery. Mum had suffered a stroke on the operating table that had paralysed the entire right-hand side of her body. We wouldn't know it at the time, but the implications of this would still be an issue to this day. So, yes, she had survived the operation, and yes, the bleeding on her brain had stopped for now, but she was still in a critical condition. From there, it was an hourly struggle for life, with Mum going in and out of consciousness and the risk of vasospasm threatening to kill off more of her brain. That critical time was to continue for another three weeks.

As the hours ticked by, we watched Mum fighting for life. The nurses came and went every two hours. They carried out their observations to measure Mum's level of consciousness. These tests are integral, especially for someone who's suffered brain injuries. Even knowing that, I felt horrible that they kept waking her up every two hours with a pinch and a light shining in her eyes. They had to shout at her, get her to try and answer questions, poke and prod her, and make sure she hadn't slipped into a coma. I think any normal person would lose the plot if someone kept waking them up every two hours for weeks on end, let alone someone who is suffering from massive brain damage.

She should have, in my opinion, been taken straight into the Intensive Care Unit (ICU) where I found out later that the level of care was much higher and where they had drugs that could help fight the vasospasm should they occur. I was unaware that the level of care in the neurological ward was nothing compared to ICU. But ICU is extremely expensive. Money seemed to came into play. But when it's weighed up with the hundreds and thousands of dollars it cost, not to mention the years of rehab afterwards, it just doesn't add up. What damage could we have prevented had that occurred at the outset? Often, short-term decisions to save money can cost us so much more in the long run. We see this play out in not only the medical arena but elsewhere as well, all the time. No money for mental health early on can cost more in the future. No money for advice on nutrition and lifestyle can cost more later. Being an advocate and pushing for the best care early on could have saved us the years of suffering, rehab, and the costs associated with this.

For days, we watched Mum drift in and out of consciousness. At this point, she could still talk. Each time she came out into a semi-lucid state, the weirdest and wildest stories came out of her mouth. One day, she'd been flying with Captain Kirk on the Starship Enterprise, soaring across the universe. We began to giggle slightly, and then hysterically, with exhaustion and stress. The tension was so high, but when a moment of levity came, we took it. Another day, she was convinced that Dad had left her for a high school sweetheart. She was really mad. Later, she thought my brother and his wife had divorced (they hadn't).

'Such a shame about you and Kara. I'm so disappointed.'

According to Mum, everyone was breaking up. It was a relationship apocalypse. We couldn't talk her out of it. Everything was muddled up in her mind. Every time she slipped back into unconsciousness more of her brain was dying, and we had no idea how much of her would be left. In these moments of crazy consciousness, we tried to be happy that she was trying to communicate. Soon after this, she would lose her ability to talk.

To me, the two hourly observations they had to do were like torture. But I knew they were important to make sure she was still with us. Every time she dropped below a certain conscious state, we knew a vasospasm was happening. We didn't know how much more brain damage she was suffering. It was like a double-edged sword: on one side the medical staff needed to test whether she was asleep or in a coma, and if so, how deep a coma she was in; but on the other hand, it also meant she never got enough sleep, which she desperately needed to recover. I felt it was like this juggling game between waking up and terrorising her, or risk her slipping into a coma.

My brothers and I drew up a plan to keep a twenty-four hour vigil. Despite the strict hospital rules, there was nothing, or no one, for that matter, that was keeping my family from being at Mum's side. As far as we were concerned, it was our right to be there, especially because of how critical she was; she could have died at any moment, and who in the hell would want to live knowing they weren't there if that moment came. So, we tied the whole family to a schedule, making sure there was one person with her twenty-four hours a day.

When I think about the hospital staff trying to send us home at night, I do have to smile. There was not a shit show in hell we would budge. We're a very nice, law-abiding family, but if you come between us, you better be ready for a big fight. The system is wrong if it tries to keep you from your loved ones, in my opinion, at least when someone is dying. *Protocol, fucking protocol.* I realised patients may need rest and timeout from their family members, but this was not the case here. Instead, it was about ensuring that she wouldn't die alone. No way was I leaving her unattended. By their reactions, I'd say they weren't used to people saying no, and we probably wouldn't have gotten away with it if it wasn't for my brothers: my brothers are quite large, muscular guys. I don't generally condone this, but they used their size on several occasions to make sure our point was heard and understood. It does raise the question: What happens to those who don't have big scary looking brothers or who aren't assertive enough? They go under the wheels, that's what.

I'm even sure there were some expletives used from time to time, as we argued our point to stay. I remember saying something along the lines of, 'I don't give a shit about your rules and regulations.'

We were there for a reason. It wasn't because we wanted to disrespect their rules, or that we have a problem with authority, it was because we knew our Mum the best, and we knew what her behaviour was like; normal or not. After our emergency department experience, quite frankly, I didn't trust anyone. In the end, we were allowed to stay, and our twenty-four hour a day schedule ensured there was always someone with her.

It was around then that Dad started to complain of heart pains. I knew it must have been the stress; he is a real homebody and doesn't like to be outside his house or away from his garden. So, we started telling him it would all be okay, stretching the truth to keep him calm.

'Mum's coming right now, Dad. You can go home.'

We did it because we were scared he was going to have a heart attack. To be honest, we loved him too and didn't want him to fall over when we needed to focus everything we had on Mum. We couldn't face losing our dad too, and we knew how close they were. He went back home to New Plymouth and left it in our hands. He was keeping the home fires burning while we got on with the business of helping Mum. It might sound selfish, or heartless, but I remember feeling the need to be hyper-vigilant, just for Mum. She needed our help, and I needed all my energy to go towards her.

Because Mum was still slipping in and out of consciousness and becoming more and more of a space cadet as time went on, she thought that because Dad wasn't there that he had run away with another woman. Mum became really distressed that Dad was cheating on her. She started going on and on about this woman called Jill. Poor Jill became the target of my mum's anger. My dad has always been a loyal and steadfast husband. In fact, he adores his wife, and he most certainly would never look anywhere else, and certainly not at seventy-six. Even though it was funny, we also knew we couldn't let Mum keep thinking like that. She needed to concentrate on getting better. To stop her worrying, we asked Dad to record a video message explaining that he wasn't running away, and that he loved her still. I should probably add in here that the woman Mum was talking about was someone Dad had dated when he was in high school, over fifty years previously... it's crazy what the brain dreams up.

As the sleep deprivation started to add up, things became really hard for us all. I just concentrated on holding it together in front of my family. My mum was always the one who looked after us all, so in her absence I now decided that it was my job to do the best I could. I indulged in my bossy sister role. I knew it was important for me to provide the family with direction: the routine, structure, and clear roles in order to keep pretending that I knew what the hell I was doing and what was going to help Mum. *Fake it 'til you make it*, as they say. Everyone needs someone to turn to in times of need, and I tried to make sure, at least in my mind, that I was that person for everyone.

In the moments I got to spend with Haisley, my then fiancé and now husband, it was another story. Then, I was a blubbering mess. All the emotional anguish that was building up inside me every day was released. I cried on his shoulder and sobbed until there was nothing left. He would hold me until it was all gone, and then I would wipe my tears and get back to it. It's really important that people understand it is okay to cry. It's okay to not be okay, as they say. It's okay to have a bad day and throw yourself on the floor and have a meltdown. But when you do it, you must make sure you let it all out, every last drop, and do it where you are safe and with a loved one who can help you. Because when you get back up again, you have to be like a clean slate, ready to dive straight back into it. Resilience is the word for this, the ability to just keep moving forward anyhow, somehow.

Being an ultra-endurance athlete means you can run for days without stopping, just putting one foot in front of the other. However, it's more than just about running and keeping the exhaustion at bay. It's all about the mindset and the determination to continue when every cell in your body is screaming at you to stop. It's the will to keep pushing when it seems like everything is against you. The ability to keep moving forwards no matter what, even if it means you have to crawl!

When you look at it like that, I'd been training to be able to cope with this challenge for years. All those endurance races where I'd pushed myself to my mental and physical limits helped me for the days, weeks, months, and even years of having high levels of discipline when it came to Mum's rehab. I remember an Aunty saying to me, when she watched me put Mum through her paces, day in day out, 'You are relentless, absolutely relentless!'

Being relentless is the only way to be when you are faced with an insurmountable challenge. Always behaving as if what you are doing is guaranteed to work: having a certainty—even if it's ridiculous—that you can do it. I wholeheartedly believe that it is *mindset* that helps us face any challenge: when we hold focus; stay on course; be persistent and consistent; show up day after day, and keep the faith, so to speak.

Chapter Six
One Full Apartment
& the Schedule

I've found that in life, business and relationships, it's important to control all the small side issues that are giving you stress. It's like that old proverb, "it is the last straw that breaks the camel's back". By itself the piece of straw is nothing, all of them by themselves are nothing. But when you start to add them all up, gradually the weight becomes too much, crippling even.

In those first few days, with all the family and friends around, I found it hard to control all the little things that were stressors. That was why my brothers and I sent Dad home. He was better off being away from all the tension. With our minds not worrying about Dad, we were able to give Mum more of our attention. Even after he left, Dawson and I kept feeding stories to Dad. We didn't want him to stress any more than was necessary and then become another problem added to the situation.

I was trying to coordinate the whole family in a foreign town. They came from all over New Zealand and Australia to see Mum. Every time I saw them, I knew some of them were thinking this was a goodbye visit. They were coming to pay their respects. It could well have been *that* time, but I was fully focused on her coming back. I tried to never let that thought surface. Call it denial, if you will, but hope is a powerful thing and having your mind focused on a positive outcome can be essential in moments like these.

I am truly grateful for my family who came to check on us. My Aunt Peggy, who was flying home to New Zealand from Australia, diverted her flights straight to Wellington so she could be by Mum's side. There were my cousins, Victoria and Kim, who ditched their work to come to Wellington. It was amazing to have them around. With many others popping in too, I felt a real battle between playing the hospitable host and giving my full attention to Mum. It didn't help that we only had a tiny little apartment to stay in.

If you can imagine this two-bedroom apartment holding me, my two brothers, and (in the first few days) my Dad. I remember one particular night, my brother, Mitchell, was on shift with Mum, and Dawson, myself, and Dad had bunked down for some well-earned sleep. Being the girl, I got the second room. Dad was on the pull-out bed and Dawson was on the couch. As I was trying to tune out the rumblings of Dad's snoring, I heard Dawson say, 'For fuck sake, Dad!' I got the hysterical giggles, as Dawson said, 'Yeah, keep laughing!'

It wasn't just the sleeping arrangements causing us stress. There are the many cups of coffee around a small table, with people perched on the makeshift bed in the lounge. I tried to put on a brave face, but I just couldn't cope well with the small talk.

I tried to fit them all into our twenty-four hour schedule, making sure they could see Mum without exhausting her too much, although most of the time she was out of it anyway. Some of the family really didn't expect her to get better. Being the stubborn one, I also have the kind of personality where I need to prove people wrong, particularly when they say something that I truly disagree with. So, when doctors or friends thought it was a hopeless case, that just made me dig my toes in further.

Sometimes when I'm towards the end of a really long run, and I'm struggling to even remember who I am and what I am doing to avoid giving up, I imagine that my loved one is relying on me to finish the race. I imagine that their life is in my hands. It is that motivation that pulls me to the finish line. Well, this was literally *that*.

I knew how important having a routine was and taking every day as it came, celebrating the fact we made it through one more day. You can't start the race thinking about the distance you're going to run. Sometimes, you can't even think about breaking it into days. You have to break it into small, sizeable chunks that you can manage: whether that be in kilometres, tens of kilometres or even minutes, whatever you need to get you through. You have to concentrate on that very next step only, keep your eyes low, and concentrate on the very next marker. Pull in your focus close so you don't get overwhelmed.

It was a principle my mother had taught me when I was standing at the start line of my longest run ever, attempting to run 2 250km in forty-two days through New Zealand. I remember standing there with my seven crew, three vehicles, and media, staring down the barrel of this huge distance... and having a panic attack. It suddenly all felt impossible. *How in the hell was I ever going to run 500km a week? What was I thinking?* The media was there ready to film my start, which I had pushed for, and now I was having a crisis of confidence. *Who the heck did I think I was?* I went over to my Mum and cried my eyes out. 'I don't think I can do this!'

She gave me this piece of advice that I have used time and again when things got tough. She said,

'Don't focus on the 2 250km. Focus on that first power pole up there. Focus on getting out of the starting gate and getting through the very first half hour, that is all you have to do right now. Once you are there, you can lift your eyes a little further to the next mile, then to lunch, then to the end of the day. Hold your focus close; don't look up too far or you will get overwhelmed.'

And she was right. That is how I got through: one mile at a time. Well that advice was becoming extremely handy right now.

So, as Mum's days in the hospital continued to pass, and family started to drift back to their own lives, my brothers and I were able to fall into our own routine. Even Haisley had to go back to work. We still had a mortgage to pay, and now on top of that we had to pay for the rent of our little apartment and all the other costs associated with being in Wellington. There were all these little incidental things we had to pay for that we'd never consider. The food increased, the transport costs went up. There was also going to be huge expenses related to her rehabilitation that I had no notion of at that stage. I, being self-employed, was suddenly unable to earn money.

One priority though was a gym membership. Dawson and I are fitness addicts. Being able to spend an hour a day working out all our fears and frustrations in the gym was crucial to our mental as well as physical wellbeing. In times of high pressure, you need to look after yourself. You need to take a break, or a nap, or go for a walk in the park, or go to the gym and let off some steam. Keep yourself watered and fed. Do what you can to keep yourself as mentally balanced as possible. As soon as I could, that's exactly what I did. For me, just having that one hour to myself in the gym was enough to take the edge off and stopped me from losing the plot. Whatever it is that helps you recover, reload, and refocus—you need to do it for yourself.

Having the schedule helped too. We all knew exactly where we were supposed to be and what we were supposed to be doing at all times of the day. If someone else was with Mum, we knew we could take time to recharge our batteries so we could get back in there and care for her. Setting little goals to keep you on track helps keep you all moving forward.

Dawson, Mitchell, and I covered the vigil between the three of us, and that's when the sleep deprivation really started to kick in. We were basically hot bedding the apartment. Whilst one of us rested, showered, ate, the other was out doing chores and getting in exercise, and the third was at Mum's bedside, watching her for any change in her state. We were still in that three-week danger period for vasospasm, so we were not in the clear in any way. She was critical and the hardest thing was knowing that each vasospasm would rob her of more of her brain. That was when we had our next major scare.

It was about six days after the partial coiling surgery, Dawson and I walked into the hospital first thing in the morning to relieve Mitchell. A nurse bailed us up outside in the corridors with her hand out, and said,

'Now I don't want you to panic …'

Now, these are the very words that would make you panic right? The nurse continued, '… but she seems to have slipped into a deep coma and the doctors are doing all they can right now.'

What would any sane person do when your mother's life is hanging in the balance? She's been sliding up and down on the consciousness scale for days, and a nurse comes to you and says that? You'd panic!

I think, in the entire journey after Mum's aneurysm, that moment was the only time I completely lost it. I felt horrible breaking emotionally like that in front of my brothers, but when you enter the room and there are around ten doctors and nurses working on your Mum trying to save her life... well... I just thought, *This is it! She's dying.* Up until that point, I'd been trying to let my anxiety out in small doses. But there was something in that one moment with the nurse that triggered me, and I couldn't hold it together anymore. I pushed past her into mum's room.

Mum was experiencing another vasospasm. No one could be sure because you can't actually see it. She was totally unresponsive. Somewhere between the last observation she had slipped deep into a coma and wasn't responding to even severe pain. It was the worst moment of my life. I was sure I was about to see her die. Unsure what to do, Dawson and I stood to the side as the doctors worked on Mum. They packaged up all her monitors, and then wheeled her out of the ward, straight up to the ICU. There they hooked her up to what looked like every monitor and machine the hospital had. Mum seemed to have tubes coming out every part of her. All of a sudden she looked very small and very old. She was intubated so she could breath and had a feed line going in too. The helplessness was overwhelming at this point.

Once in the ICU, she was put on a drug called Noradrenaline. Me being me, I went straight to the internet to learn as much as I could. Noradrenaline is a drug that drives blood pressure up. I know that seems counterintuitive when considering we were trying to stop blood from pouring into her brain, but the increased pressure stops or at least can lessen vasospasms. The vasospasms were restricting blood flow and starving the brain. In effect, they were causing death to different parts of her brain. By pushing up the blood pressure, doctors were trying to hold the blood vessels open. Usually high blood pressure is a bad thing, but in this case, it was a last-ditch effort to save her brain and her life.

This incident, at least, had one great outcome. Mum was now in ICU. She remained comatose for another twenty-four hours or so. Eventually, although she didn't come around fully, her consciousness level improved (at least temporarily) and was soon back to what seemed like peaceful-looking sleeping. We watched doctors and nurses constantly checking on Mum and adjusting her treatment. I realised that ICU was just next level, and I was totally pissed that she hadn't been in there from day one. Here they had a "Twenty-four-seven, one nurse for one patient" policy, and each patient was connected to every machine the medical staff deemed necessary. It was exactly what Mum needed: constant surveillance.

The drug, Noradrenaline, can have adverse reactions. Patients need constant monitoring when on it which is why they don't administer it in the neurological ward. It was what was saving her life right now. Mum needed those drugs, and her best chance for recovery was there in the ICU. I felt like we were back on track. I began to breathe again. But it made me wonder: if Noradrenaline had been available the entire time to stop her from suffering a vasospasm, and it is known that in the twenty-one days after an aneurysm there is an incredibly high-risk of suffering a vasospasm... why wasn't she placed in a position where that would be available for her? Answer: money of course—the cold hard truth of our medical system. It really floored me that she wasn't put into ICU straight away, and I was blown away the moment I connected all the dots. How many other patients have been in a similar situation, with a possibility of a recovery if they had access to certain drugs, methods, or support? We are lucky that we live in a first world country and not a third world country. But the notion that we have free medical support, and we will have access to what we need, and when we need it, regardless of our socio-economic status just isn't true. There are many countries far worse off, but somehow, I had this idea that in New Zealand, we would get what we needed.

It was the second time in this journey that we encountered such a problem, but it certainly wasn't going to be the last. We encountered financial constraints all the way, soon realising it is nearly always the deciding factor as to what level of care a patient receives. I'm a business owner, so I know what it's like making every dollar count. I know what it's like operating with limited resources, but it's so easy to see where we could have saved time, stress, and so much damage to Mum's mind and body if she had received the care she needed, when she needed it. It made me even more determined to be super vigilant and to be an advocate for her, to do whatever it took to get her the resources she needed. I just needed to be aware what those were.

I was determined to learn everything I needed to know about her condition. I took it upon myself to ingest as much information about everything related to brain injuries that I could: aneurysms, surgery, rehabilitation, medications, and therapies. I simply read anything that I thought would help our chances of getting her back. I wanted to bring myself up to speed with all the medical jargon the doctors were using. If I wasn't keeping up, then I was letting the team down. Slowly, I began to understand the medical lingo and, even better, I was able to ask the right questions. Because they didn't know her as well as I did, I could see things specific to her that they didn't have the time to catch.

There is nothing worse than being completely out of control and not knowing what is happening. On several occasions, I caught things the doctors and nurses had missed. In my opinion, it is important to educate yourself as much as possible, so you too can watch for danger signs, especially during critical phases when everything can change in the blink of an eye. Pushing to learn everything I could helped me to understand the predicted course of the aftermath of Mum's injury.

Chapter Seven
Getting to 21 Days

Our goal was to get Mum through the twenty-one day period of vasospasm risk alive, somehow. Nobody knew—if she survived—just how bad the brain damage would be. It seemed that every day she lost more of her brain; all we could concentrate on was survival first, rehab second. Dad was still at home looking after the house for when Mum returned. Mitchell, also a fireman like my husband Haisley, had to return to work, and Dawson and I stayed in Wellington. We all had our mission, and we all did our best. I know my husband worried about leaving me in Wellington. But one of us had to keep working to pay the bills. So he did that, and I focused on Mum.

Wake up. Eat. Get to the hospital. Swap out with Dawson. Study, study, study, as much as I could. Switch. Go to the gym. Eat. Sleep. Repeat. As I wrapped up each day on the calendar, I'd celebrate the fact we made it through.

I fell into that routine easily because routine made me feel in control; knowing what to do helped me cope. It's all about breaking the seemingly unachievable goal down into pieces you can see, measure, and achieve. I like to set my goals after the SMART GOAL Principle[2]. I try to make them specific, measurable, attainable, realistic, and timely. You have to make sure your goal is *specific* so you know exactly what it is your gunning for. *Measurable* means how are you going to measure the achievement to know when you've reached it? *Attainable* means is it doable or just a crazy notion? Do you believe you can achieve it? *Realistic*: is it humanly possible? Lastly, *Timely*: do you have a set timeframe to know when you've achieved your goal by? In our case, it was to get through the twenty-one day critical period.

Another vital element, and something I teach athletes aspiring to smash a marathon or any big challenge, is *visualisation*[3]. I cannot overstate the power of visualisation and how important it is for success in running. See yourself running the marathon. Feel it. Can you smell the excitement in the air? Picture every aspect of the preparation. What are you wearing? How are you feeling? In these visualisations, you are the boss; you aren't restricted like a normal mere mortal. You can be a superhero. You can run with the power of a lion, feeling strong and powerful. The more detail you go into in this visualisation process the better. The brain doesn't differentiate between reality and imagination, so if you visualise repeatedly, it starts to become a fait accompli. Your brain thinks it's already happened. Can you hear the positive voices in your head taking over, pushing the negative thoughts away, where

---

[2] Download this free ebook on Goal Setting by Lisa Tamati: https://bit.ly/2xvKD9L

[3] See Tamati, Lisa. "Visualisation Techniques: The Power of Imagination." https://www.lisatamati.com/blog/post/38485/VISUALISA-TION-TECHNIQUES-THE-POWER-OF-IMAGINATION/

they can't be heard? And of course: can you feel yourself smiling? Throwing your hands in the air as you cross the finish line? Can you feel the victory swelling within you? The pride puffing out your chest when you realise you did it? You ran that marathon! Visionaries are able to imagine the future and visualise the outcome they want, then attempt to make it happen.

I think visualisation is one of the most under-utilised tools; not only in running but every challenge in life. I recently spoke with a young pilot. He said visualisation was used in the academy where he learned to fly. Not only did he agree that he noticed a significant difference in his own ability when he used visualisation during his flight preparation, but he confirmed that the top performers in the academy all used visualisation daily. Coupling visualisation with the planning of your goals, utilising positive affirmations, and releasing doubts is so powerful. Not only setting the goal and creating the step-by-step method of reaching it, but committing to it, seeing yourself succeeding along the way, and celebrating when you hit milestones. None of this is rocket science, but these basic principles can see you go further than you ever thought possible.

When I think about these well-researched techniques, it reminds me about where my head was at during those three weeks when Mum was on the critical list. My family and I had no control over Mum's state at that time, but we could influence how she was treated, and we could certainly make sure she got what she needed. I could control what I studied. I learned what was to be expected and what hurdles and challenges awaited, what signs to watch out for, what dangers lurked. The more I learned, the better chance she would have once she had stabilised and was in the rehab phase.

Dawson and I were both fatiguing, and I knew it was putting a strain on the whole family. I know what it's like operating at the edge of your capabilities. Every day I could feel the high stress levels taking their toll on our minds and bodies. I remember looking up from where I sat beside Mum's bed one day, long enough to look at Mum and get my head out of whatever it was I was studying at the time. It wasn't pretty. She was connected to the machines all around her with wires and monitors everywhere, and there were tubes sticking out of her mouth.

Because Mum was intubated, her mouth was forever open. This allowed bacteria to flourish. It grew like a slime that covered her tongue. Then there were the bedsores. Because she was still completely immobile, Mum had to be moved around in the bed and repositioned regularly to prevent the onset of localised damage to the skin. I knew about bedsores before Mum's stay in hospital, but I didn't realise just how bad they can be. They can develop into sizeable holes in your skin and can trigger a host of other complications, like severe infections and even gangrene.

On top of that, there was a stent in her which drained the blood off her brain, slowly stopping the pressure rising in her skull. The stent was to stay in for as long as required, but it is usually taken out after ten to fifteen days, due to the risk of infection. With Mum, they had to leave it in longer. The doctors originally wanted to remove it earlier, but they had to be sure the pressure wouldn't rise again. Thankfully, with her in ICU, and with access to Noradrenaline, she was at least still alive.

Every day we were getting closer to our goal of surviving those first twenty-one days, but it was slow going.

There was so much we didn't know, including a lot of jargon. It was like learning to speak another language. But no matter how dry or dense the study got, I was determined to understand what was to be expected with Mum's case. I was hell bent on not being caught short again.

I looked everywhere on the internet. I read hundreds of articles, watched dozens of videos, flicked through journals, studied podcasts, and listened closely whenever I had the chance to speak to the doctors. I even snuck into the nurse's cupboard and borrowed a set of manuals on reading the signs and symptoms of stroke and aneurysm patients. I was on a mission, and I'm so glad I did it. Those manuals were a fantastic, up-to-date resource of particular signs to look out for and behaviours that could alert me to problems. They informed me on what drugs were good for what and what their side effects were. I did tonnes of reading on clinical studies, half of them a waste of time and not applicable to Mum's situation, but some of them were. I was hungry for information. I became a student by necessity of neuroscience, stroke and aneurysm rehab, and explored latest breakthroughs, possible therapies, and controversial approaches. I would recommend anyone in a similar situation to do the same. Don't stick your head in the sand and wait for the doctors to tell you what to do. Don't wait for the miraculous white pill to save you. Be prepared to do everything you can to support the body in its fight as well. I was determined to not let myself rely solely on the medical professionals, because they didn't have the time or resources to dedicate the same amount of energy that I could. Nor did they have the same motivating factor that I did: unconditional love for my mother and a determination to get her back. Research other methods, tests, supplements, do whatever it is that can shift the odds in your favour.

It's so important to remember, at times like this, no matter the odds and no matter how bleak it seems: as long as there is one ounce of hope, you have to hold onto that. With that hope, you can take the journey one step at a time. All you need is to concentrate on is the next step that's in front of you.

As I spent more time by Mum's bedside, I realised I was picking up on things the doctors were missing. Even in the ICU, with the monitors and all the bells and whistles, and with the one-on-one nurse observations, there were still things I could see that they missed. I don't say this as an attack on the medical fraternity because I am truly grateful they kept my Mum alive. I only wish to show how I felt, and the fact of the matter is, I knew my Mum. I was with her every day. I also found myself beginning to ask targeted questions. I certainly wasn't on the same playing field as the doctors, but I knew just enough to know what to say, or how to ask questions to help them see the changes in Mum's condition that I could see. I could query them on things, ask them what they thought about this and what were their thoughts on that. After our horrific experience in the emergency department, I made sure I was heard. I was her voice in the hospital, making 100% sure every decision was made with her in mind. Slowly, it started to pay off.

I know I pissed a lot of people off, and they thought I was a pain in the arse, but I don't care. This is one situation where I needed to be the squeaky wheel.

Finally, after about fifteen days, Mum had survived the biggest risk phase. We still had about a week of the high-risk period to go, but her condition had stabilised enough that the doctors were ready to try and remove the stent. The doctors explained they were careful to leave this critical instrument in as long as they could due to her condition, and the fact that it was working. But, with the risk of infection looming, it needed to come out.

Over a couple of days, they turned off the valve so it couldn't drain, and then waited to see what happened. It was a nightmare. Every time they attempted it, Mum slipped into another coma and they had to abort. She kept yo-yoing between being okay one hour and then deteriorating the next. With each attempt, the doctors had to work to keep her alive. I can still feel the fear that clutched at my stomach. We all knew the tube had to come out, but the doctors were more worried that she wouldn't survive without it. Three times they tried, and each time the attempt failed.

As the professionals gathered to consider the best course of action, they discussed with my brother and me the option of having a permanent stent inserted to replace the temporary one. It was another operation, with all the risks associated and Mum was in a fragile state. I was praying that that was not going to be necessary. They decided to try one last time. Thankfully, it was a success. Mum's condition didn't deteriorate, and she didn't slip into a coma. It was a huge relief. However, she was still not out of the woods. "Dr Google" told me that for the next ninety days, at any time, the pressure could rise without us knowing.

At this point, I was expecting them to suggest the second part of the coiling operation, which they had told us, was necessary. But the doctors decided that as she was so fragile, and all was good so far, they would leave it for later. No sooner had they removed the tubing, she was then taken out of ICU and put back into the neurological ward. Maybe I should have been happy that Mum was improving. But it felt like a big step backwards. We lost the Noradrenaline, the twenty-four hour surveillance; we lost all the monitors, oxygen, and intubation. We were back to sharing a ward with five other patients and observations only every two hours.

It felt like our safety net had been pulled out from beneath us. It was scary. I voiced my concerns. I told the doctors what I knew of her condition from the study I'd been doing. I asked if it was true that even though we were out of the risk period for vasospasm, that the first ninety days were still critical for risk of pressure building in the brain. It was true, and we all knew it. Yes, she'd survived the threat of vasospasm for so long, but she could still die. There were still so many other complications. She had no idea what was going on; she could barely speak. I think at that point Dawson's fatigue levels and mine were at an all-time high. Sharing the ward with five other people, who were all suffering their own illnesses, meant none of us got any sleep at night. But we had to step up our game. We knew that without the intense surveillance in the ICU, we had to be there constantly. At this point one of my favourite cousins, Duncan Tamati, who lives in Wellington, started supporting us. He came in every night after work, giving me and Dawson a break. He was an angel and would spend time just holding Mum's hand. Thank goodness for family support.

We were only in the Wellington neurological ward for a few days when I heard the doctors talking about sending her back to New Plymouth. *What the hell?* Taranaki Base Hospital didn't have the facilities for surgery. If anything went wrong and the pressure started going up, we'd be in trouble. She'd have to be airlifted back to Wellington. It was the whole reason she was brought to Wellington in the first place. Not to mention, we were worried about shifting her in her fragile state.

Was the downgrade from the ICU, and sending us back to New Plymouth a decision resulting from a lack of resources? Was it about the money? I gathered together what I had learned from my study to help my case. As far as I could see, she needed to be back in the ICU: it was the only way she was going to receive the care she needed to recover. If I let them move her back to New Plymouth, she would slip further and further away from recovery. We felt like we were being abandoned into the wilderness.

Chapter Eight
Home & Keeping Mum Breathing

Despite my concerns, and the opinions I voiced, Mum was airlifted back to New Plymouth by air ambulance. In their ever-efficient manner, the crew moved Mum from the Wellington Hospital to the airport and loaded her onto the plane. She was then flown north to New Plymouth and driven back to the Taranaki Base Hospital. Mum was home. We all were, but I didn't feel like celebrating. I was frustrated. I felt by moving back to New Plymouth, we were moving away from the place that Mum needed to be in most: the ICU.

There was a huge upside though: it was great being back to our support network. I could feel a huge weight lifting from my shoulders as I happily spent some time reconnecting with Haisley. When life demands that you push yourself hard, when it tests you to find where the true edges of your abilities are, it gives you the chance to learn who you really are. But you need to know where those limits are, and you need to respect them. Part of this process is knowing when and how you need to recover, and perhaps, most importantly, who you need around you to make that happen.

Despite being home, I didn't for one moment slack off the routine that Dawson and I had created in Wellington. We were straight back into it. I devoted nearly every waking moment I had to observing Mum and working towards her future rehab. At this time, she had nothing: no speech, except the odd word; no focus, she didn't know who we were most of the time; no control over any function in her body; and she needed so much sleep. Simply eating was a two-hour odyssey. We had to physically spoon feed food into her mouth. She didn't have the coordination to either hold a utensil or guide that utensil to her mouth. She would even forget to chew or swallow. The hospital food was also atrocious, so we made our own nutrient-rich concoctions to help her as best we could.

As the days ticked by, Mum's condition didn't improve at all. She still couldn't focus for more than a few seconds and was unable to move any part of her body purposefully. Even having the television on was a no-no, as it would exhaust her: all those sights, sounds, and flashing lights were just too much for her brain, and she'd fall asleep in moments. It was horrible seeing her like that, and I felt she was even going backwards, if that was possible.

I really struggled with not being able to communicate with her. Just to be able to hear how she was feeling or knowing what she was thinking would have been nice. Although she was still alive, physically, I had this sinking feeling that we had lost "Mum"—her essence, her intelligence, her sense of humour. With her being unable to speak, I had no way of knowing if she was still "in there." Despite the growing fear that she wouldn't recover, we all held hope that we would get our Mum back.

My frustration grew daily. I knew she needed the level of care, surveillance, and technology that was only available in the ICU. I felt that many of the doctors and nurses seemed to treat us like we knew nothing at all. I felt my Mum had been reduced to an elderly patient— on her way out—and that the system was simply going through the motions. So instead, I began to focus more and more of my attention on the research I'd started in Wellington. Except now I spread my search into what could be called more "functional" medicine. I looked at alternative therapies that were not accepted in New Zealand by the mainstream medical communities. I searched relentlessly for any piece of information that was even remotely connected to Mum's condition. It didn't matter how alternative or how strange it sounded, if it looked good, I would note it down and do my due diligence on it.

The more I went down this road, the more I began to analyse why she had been better in Wellington. Of course, it was the ICU. But I started to question: What was it about the ICU that was so important? Yes, the Noradrenaline helped, but that was to help raise her blood pressure and stop the vasospasm. It had to be something else. The more I thought about how Mum's condition had seemingly deteriorated since we came back to New Plymouth, the more I thought about what was different now.

It occurred to me that she'd been on a constant supply of oxygen in the ICU, and even when she was downgraded to the neurological ward, she was still given an intermittent supply. I thought, *That must be it!* And like Alice going down the rabbit hole, I began to investigate the effects of oxygen on recovery.

If you take a quick look on the internet, you can find loads and loads of reports, journals and cases of hyperbaric oxygen therapy[4]. There is a raft of information about the importance of blood flow and oxygen and the effect it has on certain types of recovery, especially brain injuries and strokes. Our body's tissues need oxygen to function, to promote healing, and to fight infection. Using hyperbaric oxygen therapy increases the oxygen uptake of cells by as much as seven times. It promotes the release of more stem cells and can decrease swelling.

I began to get excited! It was all making sense. Mum was given no oxygen while in New Plymouth, so it must have been *that* which was making the difference. I spoke to the doctors about it. They told me that Mum was fine, that her oxygen levels were nothing to be concerned with. But I couldn't let it go. Something just didn't feel right. I asked the doctor in charge of the ward if they would allow me to have supplemental oxygen on her, but I was told it wasn't necessary. I kept thinking about it until suddenly I thought of a family friend, Jez Morris, who is a sleep apnoea expert. His official title is sleep physiologist. He's helped countless patients through dozens of clinics all around New Zealand. I thought that if there was anyone who would know about oxygen, it would be him.

---

[4] Dr Harch is a leading expert on hyperbaric oxygen therapy. See https://hbot.com/

So, I reached out to him and asked if he would mind seeing Mum. I wanted him to run a sleep apnoea test[5] to see if she was, in fact, being deprived of oxygen at night while sleeping. We weren't allowed to run any tests ourselves and the doctors wouldn't permit but we did it anyway. Jez carried out his tests overnight. Bingo! He was not surprised by the horrific results. Mum had severe sleep apnoea. He explained that the situation was dire. She was having hundreds of episodes during the night. He said that she had incredibly shallow breathing whilst she slept and, at times, she had large pauses between breaths. Because of this her brain wasn't receiving enough oxygen to aid function, let alone recover. As she was sleeping eighteen to twenty hours a day, this was even more significant. Her oxygen levels were crucially hindering her recovery.

Jez also explained she was breathing in a pattern known as Cheyne-Stokes respiration. This is where the breaths are taken in gradually smaller intakes that eventuate in apnoea. He said at the lowest point her oxygen levels were at 71%. When you consider the levels should be at 98-99% this could be potentially deadly. She was, in effect, knocking off more brain cells every night.

I began to read up on Cheyne-Stokes respiration and Central Sleep Apnoea Syndrome (CSAS). It usually occurs when there is damage to the parts of your brain that control your breathing. For Mum, this likely happened during the aneurysm and subsequent stroke she suffered. For the first time in a long while,

---

[5] See: https://www.edensleep.co.nz/home for Sleep Apnoea tests.

I felt excited; it was all making sense. Perhaps she would now improve. Why was testing for sleep apnoea not standard protocol when a patient suffered any sort of a stroke? Jez said he had been advocating for just that for years, to no avail. Left untreated, sleep apnoea can greatly increase the risk of heart attacks, strokes, diabetes, heart failure, irregular heartbeat, and obesity—all of which were complications we really didn't need in her recovery. More importantly, it would make any sort of real recovery virtually impossible. I was so glad I had pushed to have the testing done, and I was extremely grateful to Jez for going out on a professional limb and being willing to ignore the rules on the ward.

This was a crucial point in her recovery, both for her physical and mental rehabilitation. However, it wouldn't be easy to access this help. I would again have to go around the doctors to make it happen. After the diagnosis, Jez ordered us a Continuous Positive Airways Pressure, or CPAP machine. This machine straps to a patient's mouth and forces air into the lungs when it detects that the person isn't breathing, as they should be. Not for the first time in Mum's recovery, I was happy that I'd broken the rules. I copped a lot of verbal flak for breaking regulations by bringing an outside consultant into the hospital. Guess what? I didn't care. If this would help Mum, then I would do it.

There are times when you feel you are completely alone on a journey like this. I approached Mum's rehab with the expectation that she would get better, that there would be a way to help her recover, that somewhere there was a solution. Inside, I have a determined little voice that often seems to believe I can make things happen, that I can beat the odds.

When you hear that tiny voice, don't allow it to be shouted down by the louder doubting voices in your head. Listen carefully and try to block the screaming naysaying voice out. Feed the voice that says *you can*. Find stories of people who have overcome challenges; read books from experts in different areas who have found ways around problems. Know that somewhere out there is an answer. Let that determination rise up within you and reject the "reality" advocates: the ones saying it can't be done. So often they can be wrong. Many amazing achievements have been led by people who ignored the negative people saying they can't.

I pushed hard for another opinion, another option. Standing alone but being up against a tidal wave of opposing opinion is difficult. Achieving a goal is about backing yourself and creating a plan, then following that plan, step by step. If you hit up against something that blocks your way, find a path to swerve around it. Keep heading for that goal, even if you see no progress for a long time. Tenacity, flexibility, hard work, a conviction that you are right and a commitment and willingness to do what others aren't will see you succeed. It's about putting one purposeful foot in front of the other.

It was, however, only to be a few days later when our hospital social worker said that if Mum was Cheyne-Stoke breathing she was not long for this world, that this was a sign she was about to die. I raced off to find Jez, panic stricken. If what the social worker was saying was right, then why hadn't he warned us? He confirmed that yes, Cheyne-Stokes respiration occurs when someone is close to death, but not only then. People could go on for a long time suffering with it and it definitely was not good. However, that didn't necessarily mean the end was near. I will be eternally grateful for the help and the advice he offered throughout this journey, and, interestingly, we later went into business together, but more about that later. We had the CPAP machine brought into Mum's ward. She was hooked up, and the nurses were trained on how to use it.

I'm not sure why the social worker had said what he said. He wasn't an expert, and he certainly got us into a real panic. It wasn't the last time I would have a run in with this person, either. There would be several more occasions where we totally butted heads.

It wasn't too long after that incident that the same social worker asked me to sign a non-resuscitation order. I remember sitting there absolutely flabbergasted. The anger was rising as I listened to what he was saying. Now, I know that the professionals have to consider quality of life. But, as I said earlier, I don't give up because the going gets tough, and as long as there is a chance, in my opinion, you fight. That might be different when you have a terminal illness, but Mum's condition wasn't terminal. There was no way I was signing the order. No matter how much pressure he wanted to exert. In my opinion, it was a way of saying, "just get rid of her." It was giving up. I'd stopped not only my own life, but also that of my family's, so we could fight for Mum's life. I was ready to throw absolutely everything we had into Mum's rehabilitation until there was absolutely no chance of Mum coming back. As far as I was concerned, we were nowhere near that point. As he sat there outlining all the factors, a big *Fuck you!* was the thought running through my mind. However, I said simply, 'No.' I continued to smile and nod as he spoke more and more about the risk of brain damage, that she could be confined to bed for the rest of her life. But when he said it was the humane thing to do, I think at that point I really did tell him to fuck off. I couldn't sit there and take that crap anymore. I had a mother to save. I am a fighter and so is my Mum, and we don't give up easily. Life is precious.

This guy, in my opinion, was unprofessional and I have a deep disdain for this type of behaviour. We saw him more and more throughout Mum's journey. I can't say those encounters were pleasant. We certainly didn't feel listened to or supported. It seemed that each time we met, he was trying to push us into a decision we didn't want: like the time he discussed getting Mum out of the hospital and into a rest home. Again, I listened to him explain how it would be better for her to be in a rest home where she could be cared for. I don't want her cared for, I thought to myself, as he continued to talk, I want her to recover! Mum was still barely capable of being awake for more than an hour at a time, she had no focus, and she definitely couldn't decide if she wanted to be shipped off to a rest home or not. But I knew my Mum, and I knew the last thing she'd want was to be placed in a rest home, thinking that we'd abandoned her. When I speak to her now about what happened back then, she is mortified to think we could have done that to her.

I dug in my heels and argued the point, until finally she was given the go-ahead to stay in the hospital for another two weeks. I felt like I'd been given an extension on a school assignment because the end was still inevitable. No matter how hard I argued, they'd moved us from the ICU in Wellington, to the neurological ward, then back to New Plymouth, and now they were trying to move us from the hospital into an aged-care facility. Whatever the case, we found those interactions incredibly frustrating. The further we travelled along this journey, the more we got the feeling that resources are often the deciding factor in how a patient is cared for, and, if I wanted to be really crass, which patients are cared for. I'm not sure if this has happened or continues to happen to other families. Although my research, and looking into cases similar to Mum's, suggest it does. It's unfair, especially when people are at their most vulnerable.

I was acutely aware of what was going on with her recovery, seeing things that seemed to get missed. I recall one particular moment when I asked a doctor a targeted question about the sleep apnoea tests. He replied, 'That's not my job. I work in surgery in the theatre.' He continued to explain, and as he did, I could see how the system worked: each specialist had their own area of expertise, and although they were all part of the system, they only concentrated on their piece of the picture. As far as I could see, there was limited interaction between them. They had meetings to discuss cases, but I felt a holistic disconnect. Nobody was looking left or right, let alone thinking outside the box. Nothing in this system is personalised: it's all algorithm based. If you display this set of problems, you get certain answers. It doesn't allow for any customisation. You have to try and maintain oversight when advocating for a loved one, because you are intimately connected to them. You will see things the professionals don't. Even if you aren't medically trained, don't discount what you can contribute to the situation.

I remember I also had an argument with the nurse whose textbooks I "borrowed." She told me it wasn't my job to worry about what was going on. As far as I was concerned, she couldn't be more wrong. I knew that in researching everything and anything that was even remotely related to what Mum was going through, I might bark up the wrong tree, it was inevitable. It always is. But if it meant I had the chance to catch things along the way, it was worth it. Just like when we discovered her sleep apnoea, knowing what was happening with her and advocating for the important tests, medications, and treatments was worth it. Giving yourself over to the system is naive and dangerous. Time and again I was told I didn't know what I was talking about. I felt underestimated, and some medical professionals often treated me like I was stupid. At the very least, I was seen as a nuisance. But I was okay with that. I wasn't prepared to accept any more mistakes in Mum's recovery if I could do anything to avoid them.

On a side note, I know it's easy for an outsider to look in on the happenings of an industry they know little about and make judgement calls. But I feel so strongly about this. People often put their heads in the sand; they just want everything taken care of for them. Health doesn't work this way. In my humble opinion, and based solely on my experience, the medical world is absolutely brilliant at trauma and surgery, but not so great when it comes to chronic illnesses. The doctors knowledge of nutrition or other therapies can be limited. I see a groundswell of change among the more proactive integrated practitioners happening though, and I hope this trend continues. I have the privilege of learning from many of the leading functional medical practitioners, and I know many of them feel frustrated in this way too.

Chapter Nine
Dealing with the System

He went behind my back! After I told him we weren't signing a non-resuscitation and argued that we wouldn't be putting Mum into an aged-care facility, the difficult social worker went behind my back and spoke to my father—in front of my mother!

Dad later told me how this guy came to him whilst he was visiting Mum and told him he had a very "forceful" family. He said we were doing the wrong thing and that Dad should sign this form so Mum could be moved into a home. He said there was no way she, or we, for that matter, would cope having her around the home. She needed care twenty-four hours a day, seven days a week.

This wasn't the first time in this journey—nor would it be the last—that people wouldn't talk *to* Mum. They treated her like she wasn't there; talking about her like she didn't exist. I can't think of anything more degrading for a human who has just suffered severe brain trauma, or any injury for that matter. I want you to understand how necessary it is to treat your loved ones as normally as you can, no matter what state they're in, and I don't just mean in hospital either. I can't stress how important it was for Mum's recovery to be surrounded by love, care, and comfort.

Due to the severe damage to her brain, Mum had very limited communication, so for most of the time we had no idea what she was thinking. But that doesn't mean she wasn't thinking. I can't imagine how she felt, laying there in bed, with a body that wouldn't move, unable to defend herself as people discussed her future over her. Imagine what it would be like with everyone around you, talking about you, and how you might not make it, and you have no way of talking back. Imagine if you had no way of asking questions or explaining how you feel. It's heartbreaking just thinking about it. As we moved further into the months after the aneurysm, I tried harder and harder to ensure the staff were talking *to* Mum, explaining what they were doing and most importantly, why they were doing it. Because the decisions were regarding *her* life, and she needed to be included even if she couldn't tell us what she wanted or how she felt at that time.

The impact of that social worker's discussion with Dad was nearly catastrophic. Remember when we told Dad to go home and leave us to look after Mum in Wellington Hospital? There was a reason for that. Mum is the love of his life. Dad can't imagine his life without the woman he loves. When he heard what the social worker was saying, he wanted to go home and do something stupid with his rifle. He was in a really fragile state, and I couldn't believe what had happened. I couldn't believe how someone could worm their way into a family unit like that and cause so much damage. I was furious. But before I reacted, I did what I was beginning to get good at: I asked for a second opinion.

I reached out to a friend of mine, Sharon, who had previously worked at the Stroke Foundation. I will never forget what she said, 'Lisa, you need to take her home. Even if she isn't with it. If she is at home, surrounded by love, she will have a much better chance of getting better. It will be really hard, but if you can do that for her, she will have the best chance of recovery.'

I have to thank her, and all the others who have helped my family and me along this journey. Their help enabled us to keep fighting for Mum's life, and I honestly believe we couldn't have done it without them. She was my lifeline in this tidal wave of people telling me we couldn't cope with Mum at home. With her support, I listened to my instincts. *Why wouldn't Mum want to be at home, surrounded by all her things and all her family? Why wouldn't we want her moved away from a clinical environment to where she could be surrounded by love?* When she encouraged us to stay strong against the opinions of others and take Mum home, it was exactly the vote of confidence we needed.

Having her there to guide and direct us through that minefield was … well, I couldn't have done it without her. She did warn us all how hard it would be, but we were committed. And she was right; it probably was one of the hardest things I've done; far harder than any Ultra. My heart broke every day seeing Mum struggle so much. Sharon was even instrumental in directing us on how to improve our house to help Mum's recovery: take out this wall, move this piece of furniture there, change the toilet so it's like this.

Once I'd gathered all the information, I went back to the social worker and told him what I thought. I was absolutely livid he had gone behind my back. I was the spokesperson for the family for a damn good reason, and I was so irritated that he had endangered my Dad in such a way. Going behind our backs was disrespectful to my Mum and potentially lethal to my Dad.

But luckily, like all things in life, not everyone is like that. There was another social worker, Jackie Price, from another department in the hospital. She had been a long-time family friend. I don't remember how or why, but one day she crossed jurisdictions and came in to check on Mum. Jackie put her butt on the line for us many times in those last weeks at the hospital. She even went straight to the boss to get us the assistance we needed. She got in big trouble for that. People like Jackie deserve a medal for advocating in a system she knows well, and that was grinding us under the wheel.

It was in the last week of Mum's hospital stay that a meeting was organised with the clinical team responsible for Mum: the consultants, doctors, physios, speech therapists, occupational therapist, head nurse, etc. The entire family was called in. As we sat down at the large table, I realised just how confronting and intimidating the situation was. We didn't understand the process, and we didn't understand how the meeting would proceed. This was a meeting to discuss her release and where she would go next. They had an agenda: get her into a rest home. We had an agenda: bring her home. We were already at odds. In fact, I felt that's what much of the journey through the hospital system was like: left in the dark with no idea what was happening or why. Again, I felt like they held all the resources. They held all the purse strings, and they were holding the power. Most of the time, it seemed that decisions were made unbeknownst to us, and they were just paying lip service by asking us what we wanted.

The meeting felt like an intensive panel interview. It felt like they held the winning hand to decide Mum's destiny. The professionals were all there to share their thoughts on how poorly Mum's recovery was going. From there, it would be decided what the best course of action was and how to proceed with her treatment, or if there would be any more treatment. They said that further treatments would not produce any positive results.

As the last of the chairs were pulled into place, and everyone shuffled themselves in, I started thinking that the family and I were fighting battles on all fronts. I felt we were fighting the lack of resources, differing opinions, and the system itself. I looked around the room: it felt clinical, impersonal, and intimidating. To make matters worse, the infamous social worker was the person in charge of the meeting. I felt my temperature rising. I'd had more than enough of this man and his games, and my brothers were starting to think that way as well. I knew that Mum was being sidelined due to her age. There were so many times that because she was over sixty-five, the first answer was to just put her in an aged-care facility.

The *elderly*. I hate this label and the way it makes older people sound so old, frail, and passed their used-by date. Why don't we just call them *older* adults? Why don't we empower them instead of putting them away in homes where their power is taken away from them? Now, I know there are many amazing facilities that care for people who need the support, but I feel it should be a last resort, or at least the decision of the person going into the facility. I know that the people who work in these places do wonderful jobs, but I wanted the very best for Mum and that was going to be having her at home with us. I guess what's important to take from this is that age shouldn't be a barrier to anything: not health, not wellbeing, and certainly not to who gets resources. I have seen so many athletes doing ultramarathons in their sixties and seventies. I learned never to judge a book by its cover. Many of them outperform younger and arguably fitter athletes simply because of their drive, determination, experience, and toughness.

The proceedings began when the social worker stood up from his seat and addressed the room. He told everyone how the meeting was going to run: that all the medical staff were going to say their part and that no questions were to be asked during their talks. He said that when they were finished, my family and I were allowed to ask questions. Sitting there, I felt like a schoolgirl who'd been dragged to the headmaster's office for being naughty. I nodded my head, but I was barely controlling my anger. It had been three months since Mum had suffered the aneurysm. I'd spent most of that time learning everything I could about what was happening in her body: studying neuroplasticity, functional neurology, physiotherapy, what medications she was on. I was eager to hear what the doctors and therapists had to say, and I was as prepared as I could be to not be drowned in big words and fancy names. I also had so many questions I wanted to ask them.

But I was also ready for battle. I felt they wanted her out of the system, and I knew they didn't believe for a minute she had a shit show in hell of improving at all. However, I was ready to argue my case, to fight for the resources we needed for her, and to fight to take her home.

As the meeting got underway, the doctor in charge of the ward said her piece, and I needed to clarify some points. I put up my hand and started asking a question. The social worker butted in, 'Stop right there. You can't ask questions now. Like I said at the start, you can only ask them at the end when the specialists have finished speaking.'

Well, Dawson, is the type of bloke who doesn't mince words and isn't intimidated by anything or anyone. He also loves his mother with a vengeance. Before I could open my mouth, my brother stood up, leaned over the table towards this social worker and said, 'You would do well to sit right back down now, and you are going to shut your fucking mouth, and my sister here is going to run the meeting from now on, and you are all going to shut up and listen.' Inside, I was grinning away to myself, stoked that my brother had backed me up in this extremely intimidating meeting. I was so proud of Dawson staring down this team of educated medical professionals. They must know how intimidating it is for the normal civilian to sit in front of a team of academics and listen as their loved one's life is decided for them. Now, Dawson has a very unorthodox way that some might say is uncivilised, but I love his honesty and his way of putting arrogant bastards in their place when need be. I love that he is not intimidated by anyone. And it damn well worked! Everyone in the room was looking down, embarrassed. The shoe was on the other foot. The man had spoken, and he wasn't taking their shit anymore.

I tried hard not to laugh as the social worker sat down immediately, with his mouth shut and eyes down. Dawson's very imposing demeanour was exactly what I needed. It gave me a break in the flow to turn the meeting around and start asking all the targeted questions that the months of study had led me to. It also gave me the confidence to hold my ground when saying I could see behaviours in Mum that the doctors hadn't. I was able to push that little harder when I asked for a specialised treatment that the doctors didn't think was necessary. The meeting inevitably went very well, and in the end, we got the outcome and all the resources we wanted.

It's sad to think how many people don't have a strong, perhaps feisty or "forceful" family who will advocate for them when they can't talk for themselves. How many just get ground under the wheels of the system, never to be heard of again?

It makes me so happy and proud to know that our family stuck together through this journey, and that we were all able to pull strength from each other, because it was crucial to Mum's recovery. The meeting was a success. We didn't have to put Mum into an aged-care facility. We were allowed to take her home. On top of that, we were allowed to have one hour in the morning and evening where caregivers would come to help out. We were also allowed to apply for funding to have the alterations to our house that I'd discussed with our friend, Sharon.

Finally, it seemed the system was working with us. It was still going to be incredibly tough, but we believed we could do it. One week later, Mum was released into our care.

Chapter Ten
Our HBOT Journey

We'd moved from the world of critical care in the hospital into the world of rehabilitation and—hopefully—recovery. In more ways than one, it was like a whole new race. Many things had changed in our lives, but there were still a few constants: we were still doing everything possible to bring Mum back to a functioning human, and I was still scouring the wonderful world of the internet for anything I could learn. But I was now turning my eye to rehabilitation, particularly for people who had suffered severe brain trauma. I was also reaching out to friends, athletes, and old colleagues for whatever ideas, or therapies I could find. I was going to leave no stone unturned, and if only one out of the hundreds of attempts we tried worked and helped Mum recover, then that was all that mattered to me.

Again, "Dr Google" was a fantastic source of information. For anyone out there wanting to know more about what is going on in their own health or the health of a loved one, I would highly recommend jumping online and seeing what you can find. But, make sure you do your due diligence; don't go jumping blindly into options. There is a lot of crap on there. However, when you see testimonials, videos, stories, clinical trials and they come up again and again on different websites, then check it out. You can listen to top scientists on podcasts or videos and learn from the best in the world. You can hop on to the best hospital websites in the world and see a plethora of options that may not have been discussed by your local doctor or at your local hospital.

The world's knowledge is growing faster than imaginable and, more than any other time, we are able to access it. We are doubling our entire knowledge base in something, like, every five years. A doctor or specialist is challenged to look further afield or they could miss out on crucial breakthroughs. I spoke with a doctor friend in the United States who said that doctors have spent years studying and have incredibly stressful, busy lives, so to try and keep up with everything new is often just outside the realm of what is possible for them. Sometimes, the system is a little slow on the pickup of new innovations: waiting years for clinical trials before pushing out a new procedure. I certainly wasn't going to wait around for that. I put as much due diligence into my research as I could, and then I took action. If I could, I would seek out a doctor to verify or ratify what I was doing. I was not going to harm Mum. But sometimes you have to weigh up the risks, and I ended up making the decisions and pursuing an option with the hopes that it would work.

It was about that time when I got back in contact with a friend I had liaised with previously through my online training company, Running Hot Coaching. His name is Ben Warren, the founder of Be Pure. He is a nutritionist and holistic health expert, and I had taken Mum to see him previously. I told him what had happened and that I was looking outside the box. I mentioned that I had stumbled across hyperbaric oxygen therapy, or HBOT. Ben had told me how beneficial this therapy could be for brain injury; he had a chamber in Havelock North. He directed me to the website www.hbot.com, run by Dr Paul Harch, one of the world's leading experts on hyperbaric oxygen therapy. I found myself enthralled by his research. I read everything he'd ever written or produced—journals, articles, reports—you name it. I watched all his videos and absorbed myself in everything I could find about HBOT.

There was one story in particular that stuck in my mind. I can still remember what it felt like watching it. It was the story of a young boy who had suffered horrific brain injuries after a car accident. He was left with severe brain damage and a tragic future. Through Dr Harch, he began treatment. At first, he was barely able to lift up his head, let alone move the rest of his body. Over a ten-month period, he worked through eighty-nine treatments in a hyperbaric oxygen chamber. I was amazed as I watched this young man gain control over his body. He eventually began to speak and then walk again[6].

My brain was going a million miles an hour: it was possible this could be crucial to Mum's recovery. *We could do this as well*, I thought. I widened my search past what Dr Harch had been doing into other treatment centres and other reports. I discovered that HBOT is

---

[6] See video entitled Curt Allen Jr.-Traumatic Brain Injury Recovery with Hyperbaric Oxygen Therapy on You Tube: https://www.youtube.com/watch?v=erXi23AC3k8&t=141s

used extensively overseas in countries, with the USA, Israel, and Germany leading the charge. There were, as I discovered, even two hyperbaric facilities in New Zealand: one in Auckland and one at Christchurch Hospitals. However, they were only funded for gangrene, burns, diabetic wounds, and crush injuries. The powers that be had decided the research was inconclusive on brain injury. Therefore, you couldn't get access to the chambers for anything like concussion, stroke, TBI, cerebral palsy, autism, multiple sclerosis, or post-traumatic stress disorder, for which the studies by Dr Harch and others had found HBOT to be beneficial.

After reading books, watching dozens of comeback videos, and learning everything from the world's leading doctors in this medicine, I was devastated I couldn't get Mum access to a chamber. But that didn't need to stop us. I'd already seen the effect the CPAP machine had on Mum's recovery in Taranaki Base Hospital, and I was no stranger to the impact of oxygen myself. In fact, I have a lot of experience with the problems and dangers of running at extreme altitudes in the Himalayas, and I knew the power of oxygen and the horrific effects when you didn't get enough.

Three years prior to Mum's aneurysm, I heard about a new race that was 222km long and over the two highest motorable mountain passes in the world in the Indian Himalayas. It started at a height of 3 600m above sea level and then went up to about 5 700m, back down to 3 600m then again up to 5 700m, as the race wove its way up and down through the passes and valleys of the Himalayas. At 5 700m above sea level you only have about one-third the oxygen that we have here at sea level. During the race's debut, the year before I attempted it, there were only three contestants, and out of those three, only one made it to the finish line. The other two ended up in hospital along with some of the crew members as well. The one who did make it, well he's not your average human being. His name is Mark Cockbain, and I met him when running through the 333km race in Niger. He also not only ran the Badwater Ultramarathon—217km with temperatures up to 57 degrees celsius and three huge mountain passes to climb—but he then climbed Mt Whitney and then ran back through Death Valley. This was for a total over 445km, doing what they call the "double crossing." So, yeah, definitely not your average human.

I talked to Mark about the race. He explained, in great detail, just how brutal it was; how hard it was to breathe, and how he still carried health issues a year later from the altitude. The temperatures could swing from minus 6 degrees celsius, to in excess of 40 degrees celsius in a matter of hours. There was pollution from the unfiltered diesel trucks that constantly drove in convoys through in this highly militarised zone, and he talked about the chaos of the organisation and the lack of any real safety measures. But then he said one thing to me that stopped me in my tracks, 'Lisa do you realise that no woman has done it, yet?'

I could be the first, I thought. Only that one thing registered with me... and there it was, my trigger. As soon as I heard that, I knew I wanted in. I'd missed the debut race but knew I could train up for the following year and give it my best shot.

I guess, along with bloody mindedness, one of my other potential weaknesses is that I have a tiny bit of an ego. For me, the option of being the first woman in the world to finish this new race across the Himalayas seemed fantastic. So ... logically ... challenge accepted! I knew I was going to have to really go outside my comfort zone. Due to my asthma, I was terrible at running uphill. I would undoubtedly be terrible at running at altitude too. I struggled with low iron and anaemia, and I was hopeless at running in the cold. But the exotic call of both the Himalayas, somewhere I hadn't been yet, and the chance to be the first woman to do this race was more than I could resist.

I set myself the goal and started working towards it, having no idea how the hell I would do it. In fact, I never do for any race, really. I just sign up in a fit of enthusiasm and excitement and live to regret it later as I try to work it out along the way. It's a good way to be, actually. You end up doing and achieving things you never would if you had only known beforehand what you were in for.

I began training hard. I managed to get a sponsor for a hypoxic training tent. The idea of this tent is to remove a portion of the oxygen from the air to allow you to prepare yourself for the lack of oxygen at altitude. I followed the rules outlined in the instructions, starting at the recommended 1 500m, and spent a few weeks sleeping in it at night, slowly increasing my altitude. But... I can be a bit impatient. I was running out of preparation time for the event, so I upped the ante. I rang my ex-husband, Gerhard, an ultra-runner from Austria with whom I have a great rivalry. We are still good friends, and I knew he had experience with the hypoxic tent. He had used one in the build up for a number of races he had competed in. I asked him, 'Do I have to follow the instructions, or can I speed it up a little bit so I can get more adapted quicker? Time is short you see.'

'Nah,' he said. 'The guidelines are for wimps. Just turn it up to 6 500m and sleep in it every night. You will be fine!'

Famous last words!

Now, ladies out there... if you have an ex-husband, never *ever* believe anything they say, because they may just be trying to kill you. Gerhard obviously was. My ex-husband is like a terminator: in fact, that is his nickname. I am sure if you cut him, no blood would come out, just that silver shape shifting stuff that you see in the movies. He is a genetic wonder. He drinks beer like it is water, coffee by the litre, he smokes, and he is one of the best ultra-endurance athletes in the world. I should have realised it may have impacted me a little more than him, but I was in a hurry ... Thanks Gerhard, that was awesome advice!

I started sleeping in this tent every night. After a couple of weeks things started going horribly wrong. I didn't know it at the time, but when there's not enough oxygen in the atmosphere, bacteria in your body goes crazy: it multiplies and spreads like wildfire. Bacteria apparently love the low-oxygen environment. I began to develop infections all over my body. Every orifice started doing things orifices shouldn't be doing: it was gross, painful, and scary. Then I started noticing I was having brain issues. Now, I obviously have a few legitimate loose screws. But this was a whole other level. My brain was doing some really strange things. In the past, I have struggled with depression, had a nervous breakdown years before, and definitely had tendencies toward an obsessive compulsive and addictive personality traits, but this was different. I was having memory loss; I couldn't remember faces. I might talk to you for an hour one day and not know you the next. My mind had missing snippets, like there was a break in the tape. So, ten weeks out from the race, and rather reluctantly, I took myself off to the doctors.

When I told him what was going on, he almost had a heart attack. He told me I was very lucky I didn't kill myself. Due to the low-oxygen environment, much of the bad bacteria in my body had proliferated and spread into full-blown infections. He questioned me about my nightly spo2 levels (the amount of oxygen running around in your blood at any given time). Usually, for most of us, it's 98-99%. Mine was frequently getting down to 70% oxygen saturation (now remember, this is the same percentage that Mum had in hospital.) This is downright deadly, and I was, in effect, killing off brain cells every night. He explained I had a hypoxic brain concussion, and to this day, I struggle to remember faces and still have some brain trauma problems.

I don't think I realised just how serious it was until he told me I could have simply not woken up. I couldn't believe I had done this to myself right before what was going to be the biggest race of my life. The doctor told me to stop using the tent. The moment I did, things started to slowly improve, but I had now sensitised my body to altitude. Maybe the moral of this little story is that you shouldn't trust your ex-husband. We actually still have a great friendship, and I'm sure he didn't mean to make me ill.

What happened with the race? Well, the following week I was competing in the Blue Mountains, Australia, doing a 100km mountain run as part of a build up for the big event. The day after the race my sponsors, The North Face, wanted to use the opportunity to do a major photo shoot. When The North Face does photo shoots it's a day long odyssey. The photo shoot started at 5:00am, and we were still going into the night. I was, by this time, very fatigued, as you might imagine, with 100km in the legs from the day before. On one of the shots, they used a flash to create this awesome effect in the photo. As the flash blinded me a little, I misjudged my step and fell. I ripped the ligaments of both sides of my ankle. Here I was, with only eight weeks to go until the toughest race of my life, with a stuffed ankle, infections everywhere, and a hypoxic brain concussion. *Awesome build up, Lisa. Way to go!*

Now back to the hyperbaric story. As I was reading Dr Harch's book *The Oxygen Revolution*[7], I knew there had to be something in this hyperbaric oxygen therapy. If a deficiency of oxygen could do such damage to the body, then it made sense that flooding the body with oxygen would have the opposite effect. Your body can take up to seven times the usual amount of oxygen when under pressure. The oxygen molecules are compressed, making them able to cross the blood brain barrier to get through to the damaged cells—that are alive but not working properly—to help with inflammation. It cannot bring

----

[7] Harch MD, Paul. (2010). *The Oxygen Revolution: Hyperbaric Oxygen Therapy*. New York: Hatherleigh Press.

the dead cells back to life, but often in brain injury there are areas around the dead tissue that are alive but not functioning properly, and these can be targeted with HBOT. The whole idea of oxygen treatment gave me hope. We now had a targeted direction for our mission for Mum, and there was nothing that was going to stop us.

I reached out to Dr Harch, who is based in the US, and was lucky enough to schedule a one-on-one consultation with one of his nurses. She was very helpful, but wouldn't provide a protocol for Mum's situation, which was what I was hoping for. They wouldn't do that without seeing Mum in person, which of course was impossible.

It was like being stuck between a rock and a hard place. There was no way we could fly Mum to the US. With a bit more research, I put together what I could from the recommended pressures, and treatment schedules of others. From all the information I found, most of it drawn from Dr. Harch's research, I drew up a plan of ninety-minute sessions, for five days a week, at 1.5 atmospheres, with an initial round of forty treatments, before a one month break, and then another forty treatments, etc. But now, I had the problem of finding and getting access to a hyperbaric chamber. I was unable to get access to the hospital ones. The decision at the hospital level was that there had to be more clinical studies done before they would open it up to people with other issues. That would mean years of trials. Quite frankly, I don't see it ever changing in New Zealand. The biggest problem is that no one can really make money from hyperbaric: there's no way to patent oxygen. With no money behind it, nothing was going to happen in a hurry. Mum couldn't wait that long. In fact, she couldn't wait at all.

Writing it out like that makes me seem like I was shooting a gun half-cocked, trying to get access to a chamber with my Mum in such a fragile state. But I like to think of it as facing your fears and doing what hasn't been done before … maybe even a lesson in trusting your instincts and just taking a leap of faith. At that point, I felt like we were out of options, and because the hyperbaric oxygen therapy seemed like the only thing on offer, I was willing to give it a go. I think once you've got to that point where you've weighed up all the risks, consequences, and possible benefits—and done your due diligence—and decided to go forward, at that point you have to stop doubting yourself. Stop asking the "what if" questions, and just get on with it.

The same can be applied to any goal, either one in training, business, or relationships. I'm a below average performer when it comes to running. I am not fast, my vo2 max (the optimal rate at which the heart, lungs and muscles can effectively use oxygen during exercise) is abysmal, but I never let a little thing like a lack of talent get in the way of my dreams. It means I have to work harder, but I can do that. It's all in the self-belief and the trust you have for yourself and your team. Just as it is in running and in business, so it seems it is in therapy as well. I've seen so many runners and entrepreneurs fail because they're half-hearted about succeeding. Because of that, they won't give their goal everything they've got, and they fail. You have to act as if everything you are doing is guaranteed to work, only with such an attitude can you hope to succeed.

At the start of all this, Mum had no idea what I was planning or doing. Much later in her recovery she had

100% trust in me, and she believed it was going to work. She would have her down days—we all did—where you would wallow in self-doubt, but the trick is to not let it go on for too long. Thankfully, Mum is as much a fighter as I am. She pulls herself together and just gets on with it. It's all in the belief, and for us, we were determined that HBOT would work.

But it wasn't as easy as just doing it. After drawing up the treatment protocol, we still had a problem. We didn't have a chamber. With the hospital ones off limits, I started looking elsewhere and found many private clinics all around the world. Then I found one in New Zealand. I heard about a woman from Kapiti called Hayley who had terminal breast cancer. Her story is remarkable. She went onto a KETO diet and used a mild hyperbaric oxygen chamber and managed to beat the cancer. It was the ratification I needed. I visited Hayley at her mild hyperbaric treatment facility. She told me her incredible survival story and why she had opened up a clinic: so that she could help others in similar situations get access to this treatment. She told me of other miraculous stories, and I was excited. I wanted to get Mum down there, but again travel would become an issue. Mum couldn't travel for more than a few minutes in a car, at this point. It would exhaust her for the whole day. I knew I couldn't get her down to Kapiti, a good four-hour drive. But Hayley and her husband were very forthcoming with information and support and encouraged me to continue. In addition to the clinic in Kapiti, there is another great facility in Mapua, near Nelson in the South Island, run by Dr Tim Ewer of Mapua Health. But again, this was too far away for us.

Then luck struck! I found a local person who just randomly had a hyperbaric chamber, and a top notch one at that. It had medical grade oxygen and could go down to a maximum of six atmospheres, not that we needed that. I asked them if I could use it for Mum, and they amazingly said yes, just sign a waiver with a lawyer that you take full responsibility and go for your life. This was a miracle really; I will forever be indebted to these people. They really were so generous, kind, and supportive.

With a plan in place, and Mum due out of hospital any day now, we set the house up for her big home coming. I was terrified and excited at the same time. I had the words ringing in my ear from that blasted social worker. He told us—in no uncertain terms—that we would fail and come running back in a matter of weeks, begging for help as she became too much for us to handle. I was determined to show him that this wouldn't be the case.

Mum arrived home! My amazing husband sourced a van that had a wheelchair ramp that meant we could transport her easily. We safely tucked her up in her own bedroom, ensconced in her family home, while we were trained on everything we needed to do by the wonderful team from Geneva (our health support service), who also provided our caregivers. With the help of our occupational therapist and our friend, Sharon, we started to come to grips with being full time nurses. It was all hands on deck. I moved back home, and my brother Dawson slept on the couch. We set about our twenty-four hour schedule again.

I will never forget the joy it bought my Dad to have his beloved wife back in his home. He went above and beyond to be the best husband he could be. For their entire marriage, Mum had done all the financial stuff, run the home, the housework, and chores, and now Dad—at the age of 77—had to step up and learn it all. The shoe was very much on the other foot, and he dedicated everything he had to her. It touched me deeply to see him struggling with his new tasks. But he was being so brave and strong for her and he was just excited to have her home, despite the state she was in. She was still alive.

The very second day we were home, I immediately took her for her first hyperbaric session. We were excited at the possibilities it presented and the chance it gave us when nothing else was on offer. But man, what a mission it was to just to get her down there and into this giant chamber. It was scary putting the mask on her and working it all out. My Dad and I were in there with her for every session. I must admit, although my family went along with it all, they were all thinking, *What the hell is she doing now?* But in true trooper style, they just followed my lead and did what I asked without arguing, glad, I think, that we were doing *something* for her.

During the first few sessions, we got a few things wrong, but slowly we got used to the routine. Mum had no idea what was happening to her and or what was going on. The sessions ticked by with nothing to show, at first. Then after about ten sessions, we had the weekend off. I started to notice she was a little bit more awake. There was a little spark behind her eyes; she was trying a few words and reacting to us just that little bit more. We powered on, day after day, week after week, until disaster.

After thirty-three treatments, the chamber had to be taken off for scheduled repairs, and we no longer had access to it. We hadn't reached our minimum forty sessions that were needed before having a month off. Then a little miracle happened. Dr Harch says that it is very common to see results when you have a break. Mum started to have a marked improvement. She suddenly started talking, and it wasn't complete gibberish. She started to move a little more. She was able to sit, crookedly, but still holding herself up. It was working: Mum was starting to come back!

Then I was desperate. Finally, I had something here, and it was working, but again I had no access and she was still in no shape to travel. So again, I went into research mode and went searching to buy a mild hyperbaric oxygen chamber.

Let me explain the difference between the mild chambers and the medical grade facilities. The medical grade ones have 100% pure oxygen delivered by tanks. However, oxygen is extremely combustible and dangerous, and there are many laws around its use. The mild hyperbaric chambers instead use oxygen concentrators. Oxygen concentrators are fundamentally different. They scrub out the other elements present in normal air and leave you with the oxygen, but the best they can do is to get to around 93% oxygen. However, there is far less danger with these units, and there are no limitations around its use. It's also not quite as effective but carries no danger of oxygen toxicity. This is when the body gets too much oxygen and that can also cause major problems. With the mild chambers, this is not a problem. The mild ones also don't have the issue of exploding. The medical grade oxygen, as I mentioned, is highly combustible, so you have to go into the chamber in only cotton clothing, and you can't take any electrical devices in. Just a small spark could cause it to explode like a bomb. The cotton clothing was safe; whereas synthetic clothing can have static and that can be enough to be big trouble. The other difference is that mild hyperbaric chambers typically only go up to between 1.3 and 1.5 atmospheres, not up to 6 atmospheres like the medical ones do. The implication here is that for different ailments the protocol is different. For example, for diabetic wounds, gas gangrene, burns, crush injuries a higher pressure is required, depending on the ailment, usually between 2 and 3 atmospheres (at sea level we are at 1 atmosphere so 2 atmospheres is twice the amount of pressure). However, for brain injury, Dr Harch found that 1.5 was the optimal pressure. We were very lucky that the mild ones would do the trick for our needs and us. So, I set out to buy one.

Now, these aren't cheap, even the mild ones can run to tens of thousands of dollars. That is the other difference with big medical grade facilities. They can cost millions to set up and run, not to mention you need hyperbaric technicians, nurses, and hyperbaric-trained doctors to legally run one. Dive companies also have them, but they are used for dive accidents only. My husband and I found a company in China that builds mild chambers that go up to 1.5 atmospheres. We re-mortgaged the house and bought one to treat Mum. It wasn't a medical-grade chamber, but it was the best we could do. Ours was not a hard chamber. They were beyond our financial means.

Instead, it was an inflatable chamber, but it would do the job nicely.

Finally, the chamber arrived, and I had my good friend, Richard Young, who had some experience and knowledge of oxygen and the system, come to help us set it all up in our spare bedroom. As we were all in there, building this chamber, we ran into a new challenge. *How the hell do you get someone as disabled as Mum into one?* This chamber has an opening at the top, which would zip closed. The space inside was the same size as a sun bed. There would be no room for us to join her in there. It was comfy enough, with a mattress and pillow. However, Mum was completely unable to help get herself into it at all, at this stage.

But like all things in this journey, it was an obstacle to overcome. And overcome it we did … with a hoist! I'd hate to think what the people around us were thinking, lowering our poor mother into this inflatable chamber every day for over an hour at a time. It must have been quite terrifying for her being in this tiny enclosed space, but she never once fought us. There were these tiny little portholes on the side that you could look through to see Mum in the chamber. So many times I'd look through, and she'd pulled the mask off her face that was feeding her the oxygen she needed. That oxygen was the whole reason for the therapy. Many times we had to depressurise the chamber, open it up, put the mask back in place, close it up, pressurise the chamber again and recommence the treatment. It was so frustrating getting all the way back up to pressure, only to look in the porthole and see she'd taken off the mask again.

Some days it was a fight the entire time, but I guess

that's what recovery is: a fight. And there was no way we were giving up, especially not when we could see signs of improvement. Mum still wasn't with it enough to realise fully what was going on, so it was our job to make that decision for her. It's so important to not only have that person driving the rehab when you set out to achieve your goals, but to know you need to be that person for others, especially when they don't want it. Sometimes, all you need is a mate beside you to walk you through the tough times. Yes, hold your hand, but not let you give up in the face of adversity.

A few years back, Haisley was running the Northburn100 race in the South Island. It's a tough 100km race, and he had been training hard for months in preparation. He rang me at the 70km mark. He had been out there for around fourteen hours. It was night. It was freezing cold, black as the inside of a cow, and a storm was howling all around him. He was really struggling, and he was reaching out for support. As his partner, I broke! I told him it was okay and that he could pull out if he wanted to. I regret saying that. I fell out of coach mode, and I went all soft on him. Because he was my partner and I loved him, I allowed him to fail when I shouldn't have. He did pull out of that race, and he regretted it. Even to this day just wishes he had pushed on through the deep dark night of hell and had finished that race. I can't help but see what I did wrong. In that instant, if I had pushed just that little bit harder, I could have made the difference, instead of giving him an out and the permission to give up. Because if you fail in that moment it will stay with you forever. When you're in that moment, all you can face is the pain, and all you can think about is a hot shower, and let's face it: we're all human. If we give ourselves a chance to take the easy road, we will.

If you're in that space and someone gives you an out, then you will take it. Sometimes, you need that person to just push you that little bit further. Whoever it is: a coach, a mentor, a parent, a friend, or in Mum's case, her daughter. It doesn't matter who it is as long as they're there, pushing you along. Over the years, I have had the privilege of having crew members get me through tough times like that by giving me some tough love and pushing me through. Now, I had to do that for Mum.

In Mum's case, I was so determined, and still am, even now. I get up every single day, even three and a half years later, and I bring that same attitude to the fight. I feel that same determination burning within me. Every time the going got tough with Mum, I would think of one thing: her life hung in the balance, and I had promised to never ever leave her side. I knew I could push my body to the limits of endurance and hold it there for days. I knew I could run hundreds and hundreds of kilometres because I wanted to. So imagine what I could achieve when love was my motivating factor: when the life of my mother was hanging in the balance. These are the conversations I still have regularly with myself.

So now we had our own chamber, and we could get my Mum back into treatment. HBOT continued to do its job. Slowly we were bringing my Mum back from the brink, very slowly but surely. Once she started to have a little more function, well then it was time for more ideas. I continued to study everything I could to just stay one step ahead of her in her rehab. As she started to have just a little bit more to work with, we could start to focus on different rehabilitation techniques. The fatigue was still our worst enemy. She slept so much. But inch-by-inch she started to gain her strength and we had little wins.

Chapter Eleven
The Reality of Rehab

Mum's rehabilitation was taking its toll on the family. It was so important for me to bring her home to us, but it was wearing us all down, just like that social worker said it would. However, he underestimated how far we could and would push ourselves. By applying the mindset of an athlete, we can operate at a level that is required for a fair amount of time if we have to. We all—my brothers included—know what it takes to push through barriers. There was no such thing as a day off, or timeout, not even Christmas Day, or birthdays. Every single day we continued the routine of trying to rehabilitate, because we knew the moment we stopped, she would slip backwards.

In the beginning, everyone was there to lend a hand. Friends, family, and neighbours all pitched in, but as the weeks turned into months, people returned to their own lives. Even the family were struggling to cope with the relentless nature of the care Mum needed. I was more accustomed to functioning with fatigue, and I knew the only way we were going to have a chance at rehabilitating Mum was to be nothing other than absolutely consistent. So I pushed harder to help out where I could, but it was taking its toll on my body. After three weeks in Wellington, three months at the Taranaki Base Hospital, and then another three months living out of Mum and Dad's house, I'd been living away from my partner for nearly seven months. Then there was the running of my businesses, which is very time intensive and growing. Nights were used to catch up with what I had missed during the day.

As we fatigued, there was also a desperate fight to keep the family together and continue to function as a team. The further we went down the road of home rehabilitation, the more we realised just how big the task was that we'd set out to achieve. The costs emotionally, financially, and physically were weighing on everybody, and I lived with this feeling of being on a battlefield, fighting not only hourly for her to improve, but also against the system. Even though we were now out of the hospital, there was absolutely no support in regard to things like physio, speech therapy, etc. Getting necessary alterations to her home so we could shower her took over a year.

For months we continued the mindless, day-to-day grind of trying to maintain her muscle strength, stretching her limbs to try and counteract her spasticity, increasing her time of being awake, increasing her ability to focus, teaching her to speak, trying to teach her to sit straight, dealing with the fact that she had no spatial awareness, no ability to work out which muscles to contract to cause a desired movement, fighting bed sores, neck problems, continence issues, the breakdown of her skin from the incontinence, constipation, bone density loss from being non-weight bearing, the drop foot starting to happen because she was in bed for 90% of the time and never put weight on her feet. The list just goes on when someone is severely disabled—things that healthy people wouldn't even be aware of. It's not just about *not* being able to walk, but not being able to wipe your own bum, or do up your own buttons, or lift your arms to put your top on, and on and on.

But we were unshakable in our belief that we could bring her back. No matter how bleak things look, you find that little voice inside you that says, *You can*. You have to ignore everything else and only listen to that: ignore all the odds, ignore the naysayers, ignore even the lack of progress, and just keep being relentless and persistent and consistent, without thinking too much. I was constantly criticised by people, 'Why are you putting her through all of this? Why don't you just let her be, make her comfortable?' That attitude infuriates me. As human beings we don't need to be comfortable, we need to be challenged. Whether you are five or one-hundred-and-five, we need to know we can improve. We need to know loved ones are helping us and powering us through the tough times. To me, letting her "be" meant no quality of life and eventual death, and for me that wasn't an option. My Mum was a strong, determined, and intelligent woman before her aneurysm. She worked full time, looked after us all, and was an amazing wife. She deserved to be given a chance to come back. One of my favourite mottos is: paying the price today, so I can do the things tomorrow that others can't. For me, it was either the pain of discipline today, or the pain of regret tomorrow. There was certainly no chance I was going to regret not trying to give my Mum her life back. Even if the road back was arduous for her, painful at times, and tough.

During the run through New Zealand a few years before, I had—as part of my fundraising mission—also decided to run a program in schools called the "K a day" challenge. The idea was that as I was running through New Zealand, I would stop in at as many schools as possible and talk to the kids about the importance of exercise, being outside, and healthy food. The kids could follow my progress online. They competed in their own challenges that included doing at least a 1km run a day while raising money for Curekids and CanTeen. I spoke at dozens of schools along the way, and the children loved it. They also learned the importance of giving back and doing things for other people.

But it wasn't just schools that got involved. Little groups and individuals throughout the country also got on board and did their own fundraising while completing different sporting challenges. I was surprised to be contacted by a couple of rest homes in New Plymouth who had decided to take up the "K a Day" challenge with their residents. This was super cool. If they couldn't do the 1km of walking a day, then they did whatever they could do.

There was one man who'd lost both legs and one arm to diabetes. All he could do was move his right arm. He decided to do laps of the rest home in his wheelchair, round and around in circles. Another man in his nineties, a veteran who loved what I was doing, decided to get out of his wheelchair and walk the length of the hallway in the home a couple of times a day. This was a massive challenge for him. There was another lady who was sadly only in her late forties and suffered from multiple sclerosis. She was basically paralysed from the neck down. She bravely decided she would, for the first time in over four years, leave the rest home and come to meet me as I ran into New Plymouth. She had to overcome her fear but did it anyway.

As I finally ran into New Plymouth after 1 400 odd kilometres of running, I was met at our coastal walkway by a huge hoard of supporters and runners, including the residents of these rest homes. It was the most heartwarming experience of the entire mission, to see these men and women happy and with a purpose. Each one had an incredible story to share.

These two facilities changed the lives of their residents. They alone made a stand against the myth that older adults do not need to have dreams or set big goals anymore. They showed that everyone needs to have a purpose in life, to feel useful, no matter what age they are.

I truly believe that no matter how old you are, you need something you can push yourself to achieve. I feel when we are comfortable, or are making the lives of older people comfortable, like so many people said I should have done with Mum, we give them permission to give up. We give them an out. We tell them it's okay to not fight anymore, that they have passed their use by date, that society no longer needs or values them. And by now I'm sure you know how I feel about that. I hope when my time comes that I will still be on a mission. I know we're all going to die at some point, that is just something we all have to accept, but until that point, we need to feel like we are moving forward, chasing goals, living out our dreams. So why not live life hard out until the day you die?

At the very end of my run through New Zealand, and after I flew back home, I was again met by the rest home residents. They had crocheted a special blanket for my fundraising and greeted me with big hugs. They followed me as I ran the final kilometres back into town from the airport to a reception held by the Mayor.

But back to Mum's story. We too were determined to prove them all wrong, especially the medical professionals who wrote her off. I know they see failures every day, and I can understand how that leads to cynicism, but to take away a person's hope just so you don't give them false hope? Well, let's just say that's a philosophy that doesn't sit well with me. As a coach, I must empower my athletes. I must believe in them. I have to know the best way forward for them, and they have to trust me and trust in the process. Now I didn't have that certainty in this area. I didn't know exactly how the process goes or what to expect, but I pretended to my family, myself, and certainly to my Mum that I did know exactly where we were going.

You have to believe things are better than they are and then make them better than they are. You can't go into something like this with a half-hearted attitude. You have to have self-belief (even if it's unfounded), and you have to have blind optimism. There is no space for doubt, you need to be wholly committed.

In the beginning, Mum had no self-determination, no actual awareness of who or what she was. This was why it was important that we acted for her. When she couldn't move her body, we'd spend hours moving it for her: stretching and mobilising joints, to do whatever we could to stop them seizing up with paralysis from the second stroke that she suffered. We had to do whatever we could to keep her recovering. At that point, I was focusing on keeping her body strong enough to rebuild once she regained conscious control.

It was such an interesting, but also, horrific journey, discovering all these things people just don't think about. There were just so many little things, and I say "little" now, but I guess at the time they didn't seem little. Just like Haisley trying to push through the 70km mark of the 100km mountain run in the dark of night, in a snowstorm, absolutely exhausted and scared. All he could think about was stopping and giving up to that seductive thought of a warm shower and bed and knowing if he kept going it would be another seemingly eternal few hours of hell. There were times when we just had to keep pushing, with nothing other than blind faith and a vision for the future that was unwavering.

Six months after the aneurysm, Mum was still completely immobile and spent most of her days in bed, only being upright when we held her up. We were given a machine from the hospital that helped her stand up, even when she was unable to sit straight, without support. It locked her in and by pumping a handle on the side of the chair; it would lift her into a standing position and hold her legs and chest in place. She hated it, but being upright brings so many benefits. Sitting is so bad for us all, and when we are upright it gives our digestion a chance to operate right, helps with bone density and in Mum's case, I believed it would help her brain recalibrate and learn what being upright and straight was about and slowly retrain her brain.

Because of all the lying down and because we had her in nappies, her skin was starting to break down due to the urine sitting against her skin. Bedsores were our constant worry and, as her skin thinned and broke, it opened up to infection. We were battling these little infections constantly. It was then that I started to look into the idea of a permanent catheter. It seemed a lot cleaner and would get rid of the skin infections. However, much like the decisions between surgeries in the first twenty-four hours after Mum's aneurysm, there was no clear best option; all options had their downfalls. We had to choose between continuing to use the nappies or putting her through surgery. And it wasn't just one operation; it was ongoing! There would be catheter changes, and she would be hooked up to external tubes and bags. If that wasn't enough, there was then a huge risk of infection with this option too because of the opening directly into the body. It didn't matter which way we looked, there was always a risk of infection with all the dangers the procedure held for someone so fragile.

There was also the fact that we were almost recreating and retraining her brain from scratch. Mum was basically "the lights are on but nobody is home." There are all these things we take for granted in everyday life that those who've suffered severe brain damage have to completely re-learn. Take eating for example. Through most the hospital stay, Mum had been fed through a tube. So essentially Mum had the food pumped straight into her stomach, but once this was removed in hospital we had to teach her to chew and swallow. We had to feed her normal food. But Mum didn't know how to eat. She would forget that she had food in her mouth, and because her mouth was closed, it would sit in there for hours, just sitting there. There were times when she would choke. A couple of times I heard her in the middle of the night struggling to breathe through the CPAP machine. I'd race to her bedside and open her mouth to see what she was choking on, and her mouth was full of all this half chewed food! No wonder she was choking. She was as helpless as a baby. We had to be constantly checking her.

Rehabilitating her was worse than teaching a baby from scratch. The software from her brain had been fried. Also, she wasn't baby sized. She wasn't in a young body, growing, and getting stronger, but in an older body losing its strength day by day. It was like starting from nothing.

When you go through adversity, you are introduced to things about yourself you never knew. You find out what's inside and what depths of reserves you have when you need to have it. Living through those early months of recovery was something else. It was like watching Mum meet herself all over again, one tiny little fragment at a time. Up until this point, Mum had been totally unaware, as far as we could tell, of anything she was going through. As Mum started coming back to an awareness of herself as a person, as we worked day in day out to teach her new things, the battle became real to her. She began to mourn the loss of her abilities. She also had to cope with the torture of trying to heal and the gruelling nature of the training we were subjecting her to.

She was slowly coming back to the world, and what a world to come back to! Imagine waking up in a world where all of a sudden you've missed six months of your life. Imagine waking up and realising that Trump had just become President of the US! Imagine being bedridden and trapped because your body doesn't move and you can't control anything. You seem all fuzzy in the head, and you can't articulate anything. You think you are making sense, but you aren't. You can't focus on anything, and you are just so tired—tired beyond belief—and you just want to sleep. Oh, and your children and caregivers are wiping your bum and washing you down every day. Your dignity is gone, and you have no idea if you will ever be able to control anything in your life again. You aren't aware that you have really been gone, but you aren't fully back yet. There is no emotional response because you can't even feel anything anymore. There is just confusion and loss.

Chapter Twelve
Lessons from a Desert

Day by day, Mum started to improve, and inch-by-inch Mum started to regain some function. Sometimes we would go months without progress and other times she would seem to regain a lot in a short time. I was using every ounce of grit and mental toughness I had developed across twenty-five years of extreme expeditions and races. I knew that the power of the mind and the body far exceeded what most people can ever understand. Maybe that's the beauty of being surrounded by people who are into extreme sports. You get to see what happens when people push themselves beyond what is considered possible. Looking back now, I can see that period in Mum's journey helped me solidify all these thoughts, and how we as people are all capable of so much more than what we think or give ourselves credit for, as long as we have people who enable us, who believe in us; as long as we have an ironclad discipline.

One of the pivotal learning catalysts for me earlier in life was an expedition I went on across the Libyan

Desert. It was a 250km crossing through unchartered territory, completely unsupported, and we had to carry everything on our backs, including our entire water supply. At the time, I was quite young and had spent five years in a relationship that wasn't good for me. My partner at the time, Paul, and I were part of a four-person expedition across the Libyan Desert. This desert is one of the most beautiful and desolate places in the world. I'd become quite isolated in this relationship, having moved across the world to live with my partner in his home country of Austria. This trip was to be the first time in a while that we'd spent any serious amount of time with people. It was so empowering to be around others again, and I loved being out in the desert.

This expedition started in an oasis, twelve hours south of Cairo, deep into the Sahara. It was insane country, with 40-plus degrees celsius during the day that would then drop to sub-zero during the night. It was illegal what we were doing, so we had to be stealthy about our exit from the oasis, waiting till late at night to disappear amongst the dunes. We had no permits to cross the Libyan Desert, and parts of it were in a closed military zone that stretches south all the way to the Libyan border. Add to this the fact that I was a Western woman in an Islamic country, and I shudder to think now of all the horrible things that could have happened to us. I had a lot of faith in our expedition leader, Alvis, who was a Yugoslavian survival expert. I'd crossed the Arabian Desert with him the week before, and we had got along well. This expedition had been a few years in the planning for Alvis and had been on his bucket list for over twenty years. There were no proper maps of this desert, and the only ones that existed were pilot maps that Alvis had somehow been able to procure from the US Military. God only knows how.

We had calculated we could only physically carry a total of twenty litres of water each. We planned to take a maximum of ten days but hoped to get through in six to seven. We'd calculated we needed to ideally complete 40-45kms a day, which meant we had about four or five days of extra water, if things went pear-shaped.

I had spent five years prior travelling the world with Paul, cycling through dozens of countries, climbing mountains and trekking, but this was way out of the known for me. I had cycled through Tunisia, which was interesting, but this was a completely different league.

Because money was always tight, I had borrowed a pair of boots for the crossing that were the wrong size. They had been the right size when my feet weren't swollen with the heat (my feet typically swell two sizes when doing Ultras in deserts. Something I never knew back then). But as we walked, they quickly became too tight which lead to horrific blisters. I had no idea of the right foods either, nor about electrolytes, or anything really. All I brought for food was nuts and chocolate bars that would prove completely inedible with no water. Even with a small amount of rations, my backpack was still 35kg. At the time, I weighed around 59 to 60kgs, so this was over half my weight. It was so heavy; I needed the guys to haul me to my feet because I couldn't get up myself. The whole expedition was on the limits of what was possible, but we were into adventure and I was always up for a challenge.

I was also very tired. We'd crossed the Arabian Desert only the week before, another 140km journey. It wasn't as extreme as this crossing would be, but it was still pretty tiring. After days getting everything together in Cairo and meeting up again with Paul who hadn't been with us in the Arabian desert, we were knackered and dehydrated before we even started. The twelve-hour dusty bumpy bus ride hadn't helped either.

As large blisters appeared on the first night, Paul was frustrated with me from the start, as he often was. I was never good enough at anything in his eyes. I wasn't fast enough. I was weak and "bloody useless" at everything, apparently. Over the years we had been together, I had put up with so much. My confidence was so low, but he was my first love. I naively thought I could fix the problems. I believed there was something wrong me and desperately wanted to please him. I had never considered leaving him or giving up and, stupidly, had never thought that this wasn't normal or that it wasn't okay to be treated this way. Years of this had decimated my personality and my strength to fight. I blamed myself for being useless. I had the belief that love could conquer all. I had also grown up with a Dad who was a hard man, who valued physical and mental strength and didn't tolerate weakness. I think, if I put my counsellor hat on, I was still trying to prove myself worthy of their pride and admiration rather than being my own person and not giving a damn what they thought.

This trek was brutal because of the heat, the extreme lack of water (recommended is a minimum of nine litres a day in such conditions), the blisters. On top of this, we had planned to do a book of our trip. Paul was the photographer, and he wanted to constantly stop to take photos. Alvis had said to him he could photograph, as long as the group didn't have to stop every time he went to set up. He would need to use our break times for photography or catch up with the group if he stopped. Paul wanted me to run around and help him so he could get the best shots, which I found out quickly I was simply unable to do, and to also keep up with the group. In the breaks, I needed to tend to my feet and recover. I had no energy to take on the extra load required to do this, and he was pissed off with me. He was a perfectionist.

On day two, as the sun dropped, we decided to keep walking, but Paul had other ideas. He was keen to take some photographs of the sunset. He left with the plan to catch up with the group in a few minutes. As time passed, I began to get more and more worried. It was getting dark, and Alvis could see I was stressed. He made the call to camp for the night, but he was pissed. Stopping now would put us behind schedule and, ultimately, every day behind schedule meant our water supplies would be stretched.

Another ten minutes after we made camp, Paul caught up with us. I was relieved, but the tension between Alvis and Paul exploded. As the argument continued, Paul's anger turned on me. Everything was my fault: the cold he had; the fact that he hadn't brought enough water, and we were all too slow. The argument never really resolved, and over the next two days the air between the members became frosty, despite the fact that we were relying on each other to make it through the desert. Obviously when you're suffering physically, mentally, and emotionally like that, you're close to breaking point, and it's really easy for tempers to flare. I chose to shut myself off and be as quiet and out of the way as I could. I knew that I needed to get out of this in one piece, and there would be time to fix our broken relationship once we were back in civilisation.

We had been making great ground up until about halfway, but on day four, all we could see were mountains that required us to go constantly up and down cliffs. We hadn't been able to see this sort of landscape on the maps, as the scale of the map didn't allow it. It was a hell of a blow because it meant we couldn't just walk across a single plateau like we had thought but would be constantly climbing. The climbing was also very rough; the surface was rocky. As soon as you thought you had a good footing, the ground would move from under you and you would skid backwards.

Add to this our—by now—dire water situation. We were all suffering extremely from a lack of water. We had all agreed to two litres a day, but I had been rationing my water more than I should have. I had been sharing a half litre extra with Paul who was bigger and needed more. I also wanted to have some spare. I was in way worse shape than I realised. I found out years later that I had done major damage to my kidneys.

We were behind schedule. We had to break between the hours of midday and 3:00pm because it was simply too hot to move. The sun was fierce, and we attempted to chase shade wherever we could. We'd take shelter by digging little holes in the sand that we could sit in and set our backpacks up to shelter us a little. Paul's mood was as blistering as the sun.

As we were hiding under our packs, the final straw broke. Paul and Alvis wandered away from us, but I could still hear them arguing. Paul had decided to continue the trip ... on his own. I was in bits, terrified, and miserable. I lay in the hot sand, tears dripping, with the sudden realisation that our relationship was over. *You're going to leave me ... after five years ... in the middle of the desert. And where is it you think you're going to leave to, right now?* He was often threatening to break up with me, so what made this time any different? But, as I watched with disbelief, he packed his things and told Alvis to look after me. He hugged me and told me it would be alright and then disappeared over a sand dune. I stared after him as I tried to comprehend what just happened. *Would he survive by himself? Would we survive without him?* We all knew we were at our physical limits, and we were teetering on the edge. All it would take was a twisted ankle or a strained muscle, and he, being alone, would die.

I started crying, right there in the middle of the desert. When I think about it now, I feel sorry for the other two. They were probably sitting there wondering how they were going to get this hysterical woman across the desert. As I was still trying to come to terms with how bizarre the whole thing was, I took a deep breath and looked at the two guys who were staring at me with a mixture of fear and worry. I had to pull myself together. I had to compartmentalise. I knew I would have to sort my life out once we got through the desert and returned home, wherever home would be now. But for now, I had to put this aside. I also knew that I was wasting valuable water by crying. I gave myself a good talking to. I stood up, told the other guys, 'You won't have any more problems with me, I promise,' and started walking.

As the sky became darker, the air became cooler, and I suddenly felt freer. The tension that had been building over the past couple of days was gone. The scenery that night was stunning. Thousands of stars looked down on us while we prepared our camp for the night. I was in the desert, but I would survive.

On the next night, and with a suddenness that was unreal, a sandstorm hit. We didn't see it coming. It hit us with a vengeance and sent us scampering for cover. We hunkered down in our sleeping bags and closed the hoods around our heads, just leaving a small space to breath. It was like nothing I had ever experienced before. The sand got into every nook and cranny there was. It was hard to breath, and I was unable to even get my water bottle out of my backpack. We wasted hours of precious night-time walking waiting for it to finish. By the end we were covered in sand: up our noses, in our ears, it even got up your bum... and into other places. We literally had to dig ourselves out. Our eyes were ravaged. But we had to keep going.

From there, Alvis set a cracking pace; he just took off. We were so far behind schedule. Without any time to stop and drink water, we just powered on. I hadn't told the others that I had been squirrelling away my water. My body was beginning to shut down, and I was struggling to keep up. We were marching across this bleak landscape that was darker than any night you've ever seen. I remember desperately trying to keep up with Alvis. All I could see was the little white flicker of his shoes as they moved back and forth in front of me, and then all of a sudden – he was gone. Before I had a chance to realise what had happened, I fell down a break in the dunes after him. We both dusted ourselves off at the bottom, but I suddenly realised how easy it would be to lose each other.

Our goal the next day was to reach the Bawiti Depression by lunchtime. I had begun to feel dizzy and weak. My vision had been blurring, and I was no longer thirsty. As the day went on, my condition deteriorated further. The first time I blacked out, I didn't know what had happened. I suddenly just found myself on the ground. I was unable to stand on my own due to the weight of the backpack, so the boys got me back up on my feet and we marched on. We knew we had ground to make up; we would be in trouble if we didn't reach Bawiti soon. Reaching this landmark would mean we would be closer to civilisation and much-needed water. I blacked out a second time, a third time, a fourth time, and a fifth time. All I knew to do was to stand up and keep moving forward somehow, like a robot, unable to think for myself or to understand the implications of what was happening to my body. Then the hallucinations started. The rocks around me turned into monsters that were trying to chase me down. My vision was closing in from the sides. Because I was so out of it, I was unable to tell Alvis how I was feeling. I don't think he realised just how bad I was until we finally stopped at the end of the plateau, with a view down onto the depression. I broke open my pack and gulped down a litre of water. I could literally feel the cells in my body begin to hydrate. Alvis breathed a sigh of relief, recognising then just where we were and knowing that we would make it out.

Trees! We continued on for another day and reached an oasis where we were able to refill our water supplies before the last push to the major oasis we were heading to. We were closer and closer to civilization. We set up camp on the last evening, and I felt peaceful. The drama with Paul seemed like a distant memory. Of course, I would have to deal with this over the next few weeks as I would detangle my life from his, but for now I just had to focus on the last night and the last day in this desert.

We made it out of the desert the following evening. But as we approached, the anxiety started to rise again. I had started to find peace out here in the desert, with nothing to focus on but moving forward. As we approached this oasis we had to go back to stealth mode. We were still illegally here, and a major military base guarded this oasis that we had to get past in order to reach the oasis proper. We waited for darkness and slowly snuck in towards the military base. I remember sticking the last lolly I had in my mouth and looking up at the guard in the tower with his machine gun as we snuck along the wall. I should have been scared but I was beyond it. We got past the guards and made it to the first little farm courtyard. A very surprised looking donkey stared at us as we jumped over the wall and carried on in towards the centre of this big oasis with over 100 000 date palms and hot springs. We hopped over another wall and past a few stray dogs. Then kids popped out and chased us along as we headed into the centre looking for shelter and food. Three very dusty, dirty, and dried out looking "tourists" had just appeared out of nowhere. This oasis was on the only road south in this area, so occasionally the odd tourist would err this way. We were no longer such an oddity.

The three of us found a little shack with a cafe sign outside saying Coca-Cola, something I had been dreaming of all week. Ordering two bottles each, we downed the first in one go. That night, as I prepared to rest my very weary body, I felt a strong desire to turn around and walk back into the desert. The pressure of having to now sort my life out was heavy. In the desert, all I had had to worry about was survival. Everything else was in the peripheral.

The next morning, I ran into Paul outside the hotel. He was safe and for that I was relieved. But the desert had given me permission and power to take my life back. It took me years to unravel all the crap in my life, but I had survived this story and lived to tell the tale. My body was a mess, my kidneys had swelled to twice their normal size, and it took me two years to physically recover properly.

I think what's most important from that expedition was that I learned to compartmentalise my emotions in times of stress. I could have stayed there, in the middle of the desert, and cried about the fact that my partner had just left me. But I didn't. It's one of those stories that has become a metaphor for so many other journeys in my life. It's a story I tell the people I coach, in order to help them get through their own desert. Of course, this doesn't mean we all have to be bulletproof all of the time. I often have meltdowns at things that happen in life, like we all do. But when shit really goes down, I go quiet and focus on what has to be done, right then.

That's exactly what I did with Mum. I'm not a surgeon or a doctor, and my area of expertise is certainly not in medicine, but I do know how to put everything aside and just function: gather knowledge, learn, and from there, take control of the situation or at least take action.

Compartmentalisation is a skill that I rate highly, especially in dire situations. It gives you the chance to block out what's unnecessary–including emotions–so you don't run around like a cabbagehead. Of course, it's important to accept that you will still have to deal with the emotional turmoil later; but it helps you to prioritise … like bringing your mother back to life.

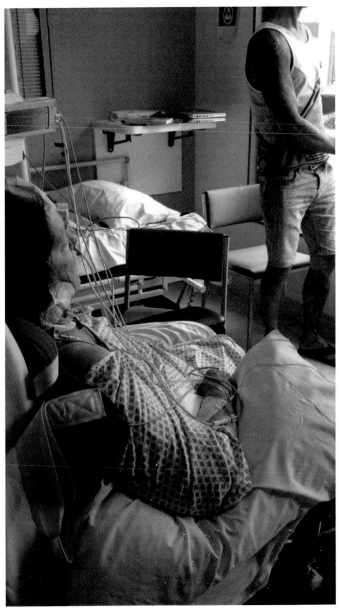

Isobel in Wellington Hospital with her son, Mitchell. This was the first time they had sat her up for a few minutes.

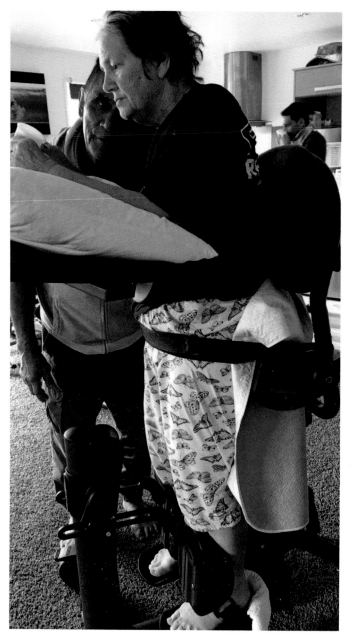

Mum and Dad spending some time being vertical.

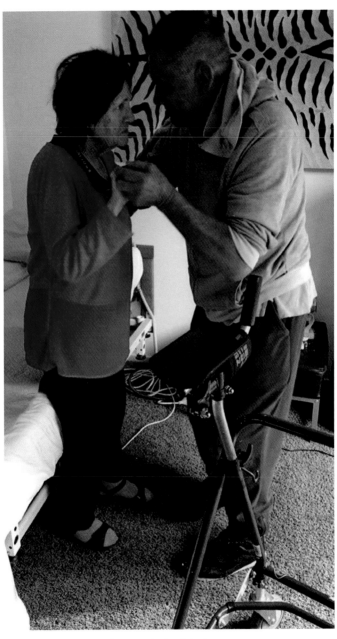

Isobel standing for the very first time – husband Cyril is ecstatic

Mum and proud daughter

Mum and daughter heading down the aisle, with Bridesmaid, Cushla, helping

Down to a walk during the La Ultra Himalayan race at extreme altitude 222 km

(That fateful shot, a split second later I fell and ripped my tendons off that left foot)

Neil, Haisley, and I with Samuel's girls at the start line of the Hawera to Havelock Run

The team Hawera to Havelock Run

Mum not enjoying standing

Learning to walk

Dawson and Isobel

Mum crewing again

Samuel Gibson, with his two daughters

Chapter Thirteen
Lessons from a Mountain

We were all getting used to what was becoming the new norm in our lives. This woman had carried me, given birth to me, cared for me, bathed me and raised me into the human I am today. And there was I, some forty-seven years later, doing all the same things for her: washing her down in the shower; wiping her after the toilet; changing her nappy.

As a family, we were all learning to get over ourselves. I think that is the number one reason older adults do get put into homes: because their family can't get over the fact of doing these intimate, daily chores. I do have to admit; I was horrified the first time I changed Mum in that hospital. But after the third or fourth time, it was easy enough to just get on with it and the shock wore off. We were all just humans who had these things to deal with. In true Tamati fashion, we started to make jokes about it. 'Pick up your dignity when you walk back out of the bathroom,' we'd say.

It was physically demanding work. I don't think I've ever realised how heavy a person is when they're an unresponsive dead weight. Mum was close to 100kgs when we started on this journey, and it was a mammoth task to move her around. We needed two people to safely move her—unless that person was my brother, Dawson, who could almost pick her up with one arm. We did have caregivers who would come around to help every morning and night for an hour to wash Mum. We only showered her once every couple of weeks in the beginning, instead relying on daily bed washes. The house wasn't really designed for that sort of situation either. The bathroom is tiny, and we couldn't get a wheelchair in there.

One day, we decided to take her to my house, which had a much bigger bathroom, and to shower her ourselves. Getting her up to my house was an adventure in itself. We had to get her out of bed and into a wheelchair: no small task. From there we could wheel her out to the van. We would lock down her chair, then unload the chair at our house and try to squeeze the chair into the house without damaging the walls. Then we could undress her and get her ready for the shower. I have to say, again, my respect for caregivers is immense. The job they do is mentally and physically demanding. It's very hard to move an adult when they are fully unable to help.

The first time we turned on the shower, she was in there, sitting on a little seat. I reached over her and turned on the water. She started whimpering like we were burning her. I reached back over and turned off the water. I checked, and it was warm water. I frowned and turned on the water again. She moaned and cried. It was horrible, and I felt terrible. Because of her brain damage for months, her nerves were super sensitive. Her brain was sending signals of pain, and she became overwhelmed with thousands of droplets of water hitting her skin. To her, it must have felt like needles were attacking her skin.

There were actually more times like that, where she'd experience something so over the top, it was painful for her. It made me realise that her brain perceived stimuli different than we did. The whole ordeal was exhausting for Mum, and us for that matter. It wiped her out for the rest of the day. It was so physically and emotionally demanding for her, that she just couldn't stay awake. When we were trying to put as much of her energy into recovery, we knew we couldn't do it every day.

After that first session, we continued to shower her in the same fashion, and like all of the routines, we got better and better each time. Her exhaustion after those early shower sessions was when I really started to learn about mental fatigue. It gave me an indication of just how hard we could push Mum in her rehabilitation. I think we all learned at that point, that mental and physical exhaustion are two completely different beasts. I'm used to physical exhaustion. I know it, I know what my body does when I get to that point, and I know how to push and push and that the mind might tell you that you can't do it anymore, but you can push through it. Long distance runners do it all the time.

In whatever time I wasn't looking after Mum, I was researching rehabilitation options. My search was getting wider and wider, and I was frequently finding many strange and wonderful inventions. Due to the severe brain damage Mum had suffered, she had a lot of spasticity in her limbs. Spasticity is a condition in which certain muscles are continuously contracted. This contraction causes stiffness or tightness of the muscles and can interfere with normal movement, and gait. Spasticity is usually caused by damage to the portion of the brain or spinal cord that controls voluntary movement. She had spasticity in her inner thighs and her arms, which meant we couldn't even open up or stretch those muscles. She still couldn't move herself, but in an attempt to stop the degeneration of her muscles, we repeated a host of basic movements to help keep the blood flowing and her limbs and joints from seizing up. One piece of tech I stumbled across was an electrode stimulation contraption. It was called a TENS Apparatus[8]. I had used them previously in rehabbing from injuries, and it worked by stimulating the muscles with electricity, causing an artificial contraction, not bought on by the brain but by the external stimulation. My thought was that it could be used in tandem with the daily movements we were doing to help build her muscle tone and potentially help fight against her body slowly locking up.

She hated the device. It could be quite painful, and her brain seemed to overreact to many forms of stimulation: from a flickering television screen to a warm shower. She also hated us moving her limbs. I had no idea if what we were doing was going to make a difference, or if any of the crazy ideas, techniques, or apparatuses were going to work. All I knew was that I had to throw everything I could at it. At the beginning, we were the ones moving

---

[8] TENS stands for transcutaneous electrical nerve stimulation device. It is used for pain relief and in physiotherapy.

her arms and legs around and around. But slowly, over time, this physical therapy started to work. She started to move them on her own, little by little. First a twitch and then a voluntary movement, and soon we were only guiding her through the movements, not doing it for her. Slowly, thanks to the hyperbaric oxygen therapy and various devices I was using, including the relentless nature of what we were doing with her, she was coming back to us.

I thought often of the lessons I learned when I ran in the Indian Himalayas doing that 222km race. It had been a pivotal race for me. I learned so much about the human psyche and myself. I then reused this for Mum's recovery. It was a lesson in not giving up, the strength of having a dedicated team, and surrounding yourself with positivity and blocking out any negativity completely.

After inadvertently nearly killing myself in the hypoxic altitude-training tent, I followed the doctor's orders to stop using it. My body did begin to recover, but I was fast running out of time to train for the race. I was about 8 to 9 weeks out from the big event when that photo-shoot catastrophe happened. Can you believe it? With torn ligaments in my ankle I only had ten weeks before the race … in the Himalayas. Great! The doctor gave me a seven-week recovery plan, and so many people advised that I shouldn't continue with the race. However, I felt my hands were tied. I'd already signed up all the sponsors, and I even had a film crew to follow me. I just couldn't back out.

I didn't run in the seven-week recovery, but I still trained. I'd not had more than three days off running for nearly fourteen years, so it was a strange sensation. But it must have been better for me than I'd realised, because as soon as the seven weeks were up, I'd recovered well and was feeling good about the upcoming race. Giving my body a break for the first time in forever was probably just the thing I needed.

We arrived in the Himalayas ten days before the event and stayed in a small village called Leh, 3 600m above sea level. I was there early to train in the conditions in an attempt to acclimatise my body to the altitude. We had about one-third of the oxygen levels at the top of the passes than at sea level. There were a group of doctors who had come from the USA to both look after us but also to study us, as no one had ever really run at this altitude for so long before, ever. They wanted to find out what the effect of low-oxygen environments would have on the human body when running 222km. Many of the doctors, and even the Indian Military that had a big presence in this area due to the proximity to many unfriendly nations, and who trained their soldiers at this altitude, said it was extremely dangerous and that people could die. The army tried to stop the race.

Being there, surrounded by all that negativity, was draining me of all my pre-race bravado. Our cameraman, who hadn't yet arrived, then rang me and said he wasn't coming. He'd found a new girlfriend and wanted to spend time with her. I scrambled to find another camera operator. But how do you find a camera operator who is crazy enough to follow us around, deep in the Himalayas, working in some pretty crazy conditions, and at short notice? I was extremely pissed off. I had obligations to my sponsors to uphold. By a miracle, one of my crew, Chris Ord, a journalist embedded in my crew from the

Geographic magazine, had mates who knew mates, and we managed with just a day or two remaining to pull off the impossible and to get a cameraman, Luke, from Australia to come.

As I continued the training, I was having blood tests regularly to see if my body was adjusting to the altitude. The doctor shook his head and said all the other runners' bodies were creating more red blood cells to compensate for the lack of oxygen, but my red blood count was going down. I explained what I'd done in the hypoxic altitude-training tent in the months leading up. He told me I had sensitised my body to the altitude and was now suffering the consequences. At that moment, I had finally got to the point where I thought I should pull out of the race. My build up had been disastrous. My ankle was still recovering, and I'd damaged my body. More importantly, my brain issues were really worrying me. There was so much negativity around the race too. It was affecting my thoughts. I was scared shitless. I went over it in my head but I couldn't quit. I had committed to sponsors and my crew, and I had worked so long and hard to get the money to come, to get the documentary going. Even if I had bitten off more than I could chew, I had a responsibility to the crew, who I'd dragged halfway across the world … so I dug deep. I told myself to buck the hell up and just do it: to stop thinking and just *do*. I pulled the team together, and I told them to shield me from everyone else: the doctors, the Indian Army, the race staff, the other runners. I said if it was something negative, I didn't want to hear it. From then on all I wanted to hear was positivity. I only wanted to hear them tell me how awesome it was going to go, how top they were at crewing, how great the race was, and how I was going to smash this.

I later heard there is a scientific name for this. It's called the Pygmalion Effect. It's when others' expectations can influence your performance. And it's so true. In fact, I use this sort of reinforcement and encouragement when coaching runners all the time. The Pygmalion Effect is basically a "fake it until you make it" strategy. It is the self-fulfilling prophecy. What you say to yourself, you bring into life. What others say to you will also have a huge influence on what you believe. You will either live up to or fall because of another's expectation. Understanding this enables you to use this strategy to help you reach large goals.

Of course, the positivity made a huge difference to how the team interacted too, and how I felt in the last day or two leading up to the race. I remember on the morning of race day, I was putting on my gear. For me, I like to think of it as putting my battle armour on. It helps build me up mentally for the race, and it enables me to create the warrior persona I need to draw strength from. It's like the New Zealand All Blacks and their haka; the power is in the mentality shift that not only scares the opponents but also emboldens the team at the same time. This sort of pre-battle routine has been proven to release testosterone into the body, and it makes you feel all the good things you need too in battle (or in my case, running 222km at altitude): bold, courageous, and determined.

I was getting dressed, thinking about my strategy. I knew I was going to make it through the first pass okay, which is an altitude of 5 600m above sea level. My major problems were going to come probably on the second pass, which was slightly higher. It was the fact that I would be going up to that extreme altitude for a second time, extremely fatigued after running, by then, around 180km or more, and not sleeping (maybe only briefly resting) for two days or more. I knew that was going to be the ultimate test.

When the race started, I was off, pacing myself slowly, exactly like the battle plan. I scaled the first pass fine. Although I did experience vomiting on the way up, everything went okay. The climb up the pass wasn't the pristine mountain run I had in my mind: far from it. Before coming to this part of India, I had this image in my head that it would be clear air, mountaintops, and snowy paths. But the reality was very different. We were running on a highway (I use that term lightly; it's a single lane cliff side trail): one of the most dangerous stretches of road in the world, through the mountains. This area happened to be a highly militarised area that was, to say the least, somewhat unstable and dangerous. Huge long convoys of trucks would pass by forty or fifty at a time on a single metal road with drop offs down cliffs on one side and shear walls on the other. I had to dodge trucks that were spewing unfiltered diesel fumes and dust in the air. They passed without any consideration. They didn't care about these crazy Westerners, running on the side of the road, and why the hell should they. So, on top of the fact that there's only around 30% of the oxygen content in the air up at that altitude, I also had to battle with extreme diesel pollution as well. This worked a treat for my asthma!

I continued down the other side. After suffering an asthma attack midway down from trying to go too fast,

I descended into the first valley. At about thirty hours into the race, on the morning of the second day, we were passing through a steep ravine in a valley, before the second climb. The heat was so intense I passed out with heat stroke. My crew rushed over and got me off the road and into the crew car, doing everything they could to cool me down. Not only did we have to cope with the freezing temperatures in the Himalayas but also the intense heat. The swings in temperature made it extra tough going! The mountain passes were below zero, but it was over forty degrees celsius in the valleys. My crew helped cool me down as best they could, got me to drink some water, and let me lie down for twenty minutes. Then they got me back on my feet and back into the race that was now down to a snail's pace, a walk not a run. I kept grinding my way slowly through the valley and started the long climb up the other side. And just as I thought before the race, this is where the real problems started.

From the bottom of the first valley to the top of the second pass, it was 35km up the side of the mountains. In running, in business, and in life, I believe the only barrier to your success is in your head, and funnily enough, the only answer to your success is in there as well. In races I have these two characters doing battle in my head. I call them the Lion and the Snake. The Lion is full of courage, guts; he is brave and strong. The Snake is the one putting doubts in your mind, the one telling you, *You can't do it*, the one asking you, *who the hell do you think you are, you loser*. The Snake is the one who tempts you constantly with thoughts like, *why are you doing this, it's impossible, just give up*. They're always fighting for control of your mind, and it's up to you which one you feed.

In daily life, I try as much as possible to feed the Lion. But when you are fatigued beyond belief, sick, unable to breath, sleep deprived, and fearful, it gets harder and harder to listen to the Lion. As I started up this long, straight climb, the Snake slithered in and started putting negative thoughts in my mind. The Snake was telling me there was no way I would be able to handle that amount of climbing, that going to that altitude with the accompanying oxygen deficit was going to break me. Then they both began to argue. The Snake started bargaining with me. *If you give up now, you can end all this pain.* The Lion is saying, *Come on, Lisa. Just make it to the next marker. Now go for the next one.* If you know anything about endurance running, you know that when the bargaining begins you have internal battles as well as the external ones. This negativity is swirling in my head. I do not actually believe anymore that I can still make it. But because I felt so indebted to my crew, and because they'd done such a brilliant job of pumping me full of positivity before the race, I didn't tell them I was struggling. I didn't want to let them down, so I kept pushing, trying not to think but to just *do*.

As I moved higher and higher, the intense heat slowly dropped away to sub-zero temperatures, and that's when the snowstorm hit. My team started putting layer after layer of clothing on me as we climbed higher and higher, until I was wearing everything we had. I looked like the Michelin man. By that stage I was no longer running at all. In fact, I wasn't even power walking. I was crawling along at just 3km per hour. The team did everything they could to help me. Every 100 to 200 or so metres they would throw down a little stool and let me catch my breath, while they massaged me, huddled around me, and tried to keep me warm. I was suffering badly from asthma, and it was getting desperate. In my zombie state, they would push me up on my feet and send me on my way.

For hours I moved like this. One hundred metres forward, stop and have a break to catch my breath. Get up and walk another hundred or two metres forward, stop and have a break. By then, I was forty hours-plus deep into the race and hypothermia was beginning to set in. To make matters even worse, those horrific army truck convoys kept coming through on a regular basis in the storm, blowing their unfiltered diesel straight into our lungs. I just couldn't breathe in any more air and collapsed again, suffocating from the asthma, pollution, the freezing coldness of the air, and the lack of oxygen. In this moment, on top of it all, I lost it and started to panic.

There is nothing more terrifying than not being able to get your next breath, and I know that when I have an asthma attack, remaining calm is crucial to controlling it. But I lost the plot. My crew sat me down again on the stool and gave me asthma medications, but the inhalers weren't really working at that altitude. They tried to calm and reassure me. As the trucks passed, I started to be able to breathe. My crew had been about to ring the medics. From the start, I had told them never get the medics unless I am on my way out because they would pull me from the race, and I can't have that. I stood back up and kept inching forward.

Another hour of battling later, and I remember looking up through the swirling snow and muttering to one of my crew, Chris Ord, 'I'm almost there, only 2km to go I think.' Josh, one of my other crew, went off and tried to calculate exactly where we were and how far it really was. He came rushing back, 'I am sorry, Lis,' says Josh. 'It's 6km to go.'

That was the last straw... I broke. Mentally, I lost it. I fell on the ground in the snow and cried, 'I can't do it! I am sorry guys but that's it. I can't go on.'

Six kilometres at that speed meant another two hours of this torture, unable to breath. I knew I'd found my breaking point, and I didn't have anything left. The rest of the crew got out of the van and huddled around me. They told me it was okay, that I'd done my best and that they were all really proud of me. They had been my rock and had been there for me every step of the way. They, too, were knackered and freezing. The race had taken its toll not only on me but on them as well. They patted me on the back and told me it was all okay, and that gave me permission to give in to the failure. There often comes a point in every ultramarathon when you think, *I can't take another step*, and you just want to lie down and die. Some races, figuratively speaking (and in others quite literally) if someone says to you: "It's okay to give up" then you have your permission to fail.

Just at that critical point in my race, Chris walked through the crew and sat down on the snow in front of me. He grabbed me by the shoulders and shook me. I could tell he wanted to slap me, but he resisted. Instead, he gripped me hard and said, 'There is no fucking way I am going to let you fail now. After all you've been through preparing for this. You can't fail when you're this close. You are going to get your sorry arse off the ground and move, and I am going to walk with you every step of the way right to the top. I am not letting you give up!'

He grabbed me by the hand and started pulling me to my feet. And that's exactly what he did. Josh also came out and walked with me. I felt the power of their commitment as they marched beside me through the storm, holding my hand, reassuring me and keeping me moving. For me, it was a defining moment in my life. To have this support, to have people around me who literally would walk through hell with me to help me was such a phenomenal experience. They helped me to the top of the pass, and it was no mean feat for either of them, either. They, too, had run and walked miles with me. They had no sleep. They were battling through their own fatigue, headaches from the altitude, and much more. Yet here they were still resolutely supporting me in my race. Dedicated to the end. Two hours later we reached the top of Tang Lang La Pass.

The snowstorm became wild and fierce, and we were called via the radios to get off the mountain. The race director had ordered everyone off until the storm passed. I still had 33km to go to the finish line, but it was all downhill, and I knew I was going to be okay. We did as the race director said and drove back down. We hunkered down in a stinking little shelter next to an open toilet with the other crews. A couple of hours later, in the early hours of the next day as the storm eased somewhat, and we were allowed back out. We headed back to the top to complete that last 33km, but I'd broken through the mental barrier. The hardest part was done. My defining moment had passed, and my mates had got me through it. From there, I continued on and finished the race.

I wasn't the first woman home. The winner of the whole race was Sharyn Gayter from England, a fifty-five-year-old asthmatic. She happens to be a multiple world record holder, so I was quite happy to finish as the second woman home and fourth overall, in fifty-three hours and five minutes. My team and I had left nothing out there. We had given it our all and had conquered the race, and I was damn proud of us all.

There were so many lessons to learn in that race, and so much of it is applicable beyond running. I guess the moral of the story is that you should face your fears, block out negativity, prepare as best you can, and then just take action and keep moving forward somehow. It is also about how crucial teamwork and support is and that it's okay to break down, but you have to stand back up and go again. Having that person who will give you a figurative slap at the right moment is critical. Surround yourself with people who will stick by you when all you want to do is give up.

All through the journey after Mum's aneurysm, I made sure I was that person for her, along with my family. It was brutal and unrelenting, and we had no real idea how far we could go in Mum's rehab and what was possible or not. We were told in no uncertain terms that a full recovery was impossible, and yet others told us it was. I always choose to listen to the latter in everything I do. Have unrealistic expectations because only by having these can we achieve the seemingly unachievable.

Chapter Fourteen
Mum Slowly Returns to Us

It wasn't one monumental shift where everything changed and suddenly Mum was there. No, it was more of a series of little breakthroughs that all started to add up. It was like having one big tick of approval that what we were doing was paying off. After months and months of repeating the treatments, we could see that is was working, and maybe like the Pygmalion Effect of the pre-race positivity from the Himalayas, the success spurred us on to work harder. But as more of her consciousness came back, I began to realise just how much work we had ahead of us. New sets of problems would present themselves, things we hadn't thought of or even considered being an issue.

One of the first breakthroughs was the day she spoke. This was fairly early on, and she still didn't have much self-determination, not even when it came to self-preservation. I had made her a hot water bottle, and put it on her tummy, as it was cold outside. To my horror I heard later that it had been too hot and had burnt her. Because she didn't know to move the hot water bottle, she was unable to stop it.

Another day, I was helping her into bed for an afternoon nap. I sat her down on the bed and began undressing her. All of a sudden, she started rocking with these tiny movements on the bed, back and forth, as she managed to raise her arm enough to point at the window. She even said, 'Window.' She was so frustrated because she wanted the window open. I was ecstatic because it was the first communicated sign of wanting something for herself, and it meant there was something going on in her brain: frustration and little movements and a desire to get what you want means you are waking up. I was so stoked. But I never let anything be that easy for her. I said, 'If you want the window open, you have to go over there and open it. I am going to help you.' I sat on the bed and pushed and pulled her onto my lap. I stuck her feet on mine, and I hauled myself up with her on my feet, just like my Dad had done with me as a little girl. I would always stand on his feet, and he would dance around the room. I used my body to move Mum and I closer to the window. It wasn't pretty or easy, but I wanted to get her to take those few steps so she could remember what it felt like to be upright and moving and doing something she wanted. I had a hell of a job keeping her upright because she was like a ragdoll. In between hysterical laughing, much grunting, and breathlessness, I managed to get her to the window and made her lift her arm up to open it. In this intimate little moment, I let humour be our strength. Helping her to move in any which way made her see she could do things, even if she was not holding herself up quite yet. It was one of those silly little moments when I realised we were making progress, and it was special. She was starting to have the will again, and I could see my Mum coming back to us.

It was unbelievable how much concentration and energy she needed to do even the tiniest of things, things you and I, as functioning adults, would just take for granted. One day, Dawson and I were trying to get Mum to sit up in bed. It was a mammoth task. Just to be able to hold herself upright on the bed without flopping to one side took so much out of her. The aneurysm had made her brain's balance systems go all to hell. Her spatial awareness was wiped out. She had no idea where her body started or stopped or where she was in space. One of the weird things her brain did was to tell her that she was sitting straight when she was actually leaning right over. For months, I would work with her every day in front of a mirror correcting her and showing her visually how bent over she was. After months of repetition her brain started to reshuffle itself.

This is called neuroplasticity[9]. It's where the brain adapts to the changing stimuli. Often these little things would have to be repeated thousands, if not tens of thousands of times, until the brain started to re-learn. We were consistent. It's easy to give up during this

---

[9] From the Macquarie Dictionary. A definition of neuroplasticity :
noun the ability of the brain to change, both in physical structure and in functional organisation, in response to experience, such that functions believed previously to be supported only by particular areas of the brain become supported instead by other areas.

phase, when you don't see progress week in and week out. One of the real keys to Mum's success is that we never compared or measured regularly. Months would go by and then we would finally look back and see just how far we had come. We would never let frustration and despair, which there was a lot of, stop us from blindly continuing the work.

Another magic moment happened when we had her home just two or three months. My brother and I were putting her to bed one evening after having her sit up and eat dinner at the table (a mission in itself). We had her on a big walking frame, and one would push and the other would be behind her holding her up in case she stumbled. There was still no self-propulsion, but when I pulled her forward her legs would move. As we got near her bedroom, we thought we would try her without the walker, for just a step or two to the bed. When Dawson was there, I was able to risk more than when it was just Mum and I alone. He had the strength to hold her weight completely if need be. Dawson held her half up, and we were trying to make her walk. She was like a ragdoll but trying to take a step. Finally, she made it over to the bed and collapsed, exhausted. She turned to us and said, 'Well, my equilibrium seems to be a little off.'

Now, at this point she hadn't uttered more than a single word or two. All of a sudden this fully formed complex sentence, using big words, just falls out of her mouth. Dawson and I looked at each with our mouths open, ecstatic, because although she then went quiet again, we knew with certainty she was in there somewhere. I even wrote that quote down and made sure to tell the neurosurgeon on the next visit. He said, 'Well, there is hope. There is intelligence still there. There is a lot going on in her head, and as the inflammation subsides and time heals, she just might be able to speak again, somewhat normally. Keep working hard. You have a chance.'

As Mum continued to improve, her speech became more fluid, though only when she wasn't fatigued. One night, while putting her to bed, I asked her about one of her long-lost cousins who had recently reconnected. She proceeded to rattle off all this information about a person she knew from sixty years prior. She just kept going and going, so much so that I had to grab my phone and film it. It was fantastic. Shortly after that, Mum's ability to hold conversations increased. Only short ones, but it didn't matter. She was talking! After ten months of having no real understanding of what she was thinking or how she was feeling, it was such a relief to be able to talk with her. It felt like some sort of normality was coming back into our lives.

I asked her a lot of questions. I quizzed her to see what she could remember, with the aim that I could start kicking her brain's recovery up a notch by providing her things to think about and giving her little tasks. It was so good for her to be at home, surrounded by all of her worldly possessions. I'd hoped that the photos, furniture, and familiar environment that she could relate to would help jog memories, not to mention being surrounded by love and family. For us, it was so important to have control of that part of her recovery. I couldn't even imagine what it would have been like for her, and how detrimental to her state of being, if she'd started coming back to awareness in a care facility that she didn't recognise, with faces she didn't know.

She told me later there was a period of roughly eight months where she couldn't remember a single thing. I told her she was lucky she didn't remember, that it was horrific, and I was grateful that she was completely unaware of what she had been through and what we had been through with her. It felt so good just to have a few words from Mum. It's those little everyday things that you take for granted that I missed the most. She still wasn't what you would call talkative. Her energy and focus dictated how much she could speak, but she was there. I craved hearing her voice. I asked her what her first memories were after the aneurysm, and she described being in the hyperbaric chamber. For me, that was another point along the journey that I was able to celebrate. To hear that her first memory was the oxygen therapy suggested to me that this was a significant element in her recovery.

As Mum began to come back to us, she struggled to get over the fact that we were looking after her. For much of her career, Mum had worked with disadvantaged youths, including some with physical disabilities, but mostly those with learning disabilities. She fostered those who fell through the cracks of the education system and showed them that they were more than they thought. Mum taught the basics of reading and writing to those who thought themselves too dumb to learn, and was always looking for new ways of teaching, thinking, and fostering in them the same belief she felt. When no one believed in them, she stood by them.

Mum spent her life helping those who couldn't help themselves, so I think for her to wake up and realise she'd missed eight months of her life and find that her children were completely looking after her was a bit hard for her to handle. But, like the rest of us, she had to get over it. She would leave her dignity at the door of the toilet or shower and pick it up again on the way out. She never once considered herself a burden, but knew she had to get better so she could care for herself again. It gave her determination to fight, having that dream of getting back to being independent.

So much had changed in her life, and we were doing our best to return to normal, or as close to normal as we could. Looking at Mum one day, I began to think that I wanted her to look like Mum again. She had always been an elegant lady. She loved getting her hair done, and she always looked lovely, with beautiful nails and clothes. But since the surgery, her hair was all over the place. Early on, the doctors had had to shave her head to put the stent in. Even though it had been months ago, the first thing you noticed was the massive chunk of hair missing. She just looked like she had been through the ringer.

We hadn't really been focused too much on Mum's personal grooming. Early on we were just surviving and managing basic bathing. In the hospital, Mum's hair had been plastered between her and the bed for weeks. The oil was building up, and she was looking so much older than she had before the aneurysm. Richard and Cushla, our family friends, were visiting their own mother in a different ward. She had broken her leg and wasn't allowed to leave her bed for a few weeks. They had worked out a way to wash her hair that didn't involve leaving the bed. I wanted to do something nice for Mum. Even though, at this early point, she wasn't conscious, I knew this small act would make her feel better. Also, she would have been horrified to have seen her unwashed hair. They arrived into the ward with a bucket, a plastic cup, shampoo, conditioner and a towel. Using the hospital side tables, you know, the white ones on wheels that slide your meal to you. They wiggled Mum a little up the bed. Using Dawson to hold Mum's head up, Richard and Cushla began to give Mum a hair wash and head massage. It's these little things that mean so much.

With Mum now long out of the hospital, and enjoying a shower most days, we decided it was time she had a little pampering. We reached out to a hairdresser, Rachael Utumapu. She is one cool chick: a fire fighter as well as a hairstylist. She arrived at the house and gave Mum a haircut. Mum instantly looked like herself again. It's amazing how much of a difference something as small as a haircut can make to perception, both other people's perception of you, and more importantly, your perception of yourself. It was helpful having those interactions with people, other than the family, for Mum. It gave her the opportunity to talk more, and just like the haircut, it helped make her feel better about herself which, of course, helped create more positivity in her recovery.

We tried as much as we could to balance catch ups with people, which exhausted Mum, with time to allow her to rest. We tried to make links between what happened in the hospital with her life now. One day at home, we had a visit from a mum and daughter who we had met in New Plymouth Hospital. Hanna was a fourteen-year-old vibrant girl who has cerebral palsy. Dawson had really connected with Hanna and her mum, Anneke, whilst we were at the hospital, so he had invited them over to see how far Mum had come.

At the time, Hanna was really struggling with her feet and had had numerous operations. She was in her wheelchair sitting next to Mum, talking. It was such a beautiful experience seeing Mum connect with Hanna. With Mum still unable to control much of her body, it was perfect for them to be able to talk and share their common ground. It helped give them some sort of normalcy, knowing that there was someone going through similar problems. There was the pair of them, both in wheelchairs, just talking and enjoying each other's company. The Isobel who was once a teacher of young people came shining through a little in Mum that day.

After that first meeting, Hanna and her mum came over regularly to see Mum. As a bonus, Anneke was always bringing food with her. Her cooking is terrific, and it was perfectly timed. I was struggling to cook good meals in the little time I had left around Mum's rehabilitation. It seemed just when I was about to run out, Anneke and Hanna would knock at the front door with casseroles, cakes, and all sorts of tasty things to fill the fridge with. Anneke was also a wealth of knowledge in how to approach funding for all sorts of things, including renovations and equipment for rehabilitation. She pointed out where we should look, what we should apply for and how to do it. We were eight months into Mum's journey after the aneurysm and we were making every dollar stretch as far as we could, so the prospect of funding to aid Mum was too exciting to pass up.

I am so grateful for the people who offered to help out where they could along the way. They might not know it, but their help really gave us strength at times when we needed it. It was always the little niceties that made the difference, like Anneke's cooking, Richard and Cushla's hair washing, and Rachel's haircut. They were the things we didn't realise we needed until we had them, and they made a world of difference to us, and of course to Mum's recovery. As far as I am concerned, recovery is built on hope, and these people, with all their support, gave us more hope to continue. But we weren't stepping forward into the dark with blind faith anymore, because having Mum lucid again gave us all the jolt of energy we needed to push harder. We knew we still had such a long way to go. But we were going to make it, and we knew it.

Chapter Fifteen
Building Strength

Mum continued to improve, but the pace was excruciatingly slow. Even the tiniest things that we take for granted and do without thinking required all of her concentration. After a few moments, she would exhaust herself and have to take a break. I, on the other hand, do everything at double speed. I sometimes feel like I need to, just to keep my head above water with the workload I have. I guess that it is just the impatient side of my personality. But because of that, I would get so frustrated. Not at Mum, but at the aneurysm, for being the reason she was not able to do the simplest movement.

When you are retraining the brain, you have to have the patience of a saint and the endurance of the toughest ultra-athlete. I have worked with hundreds of athletes as a coach, but it was so hard to change my technique and mindset to working with someone who'd suffered brain damage. It's a different ball game. The speed of learning is so slow. You literally have to repeat movement, patterns or procedures over and over, thousands of times before they sink in. Even then, a day would pass, and she'd forget again and we would be at square one the next day. Every single part of every single movement had to be relearned. Her brain fatigue limits also meant I would want to keep pushing but would be resigned to give her breaks, especially after any concentrated learning. Sometimes that would mean we'd stop after every thirty seconds, at the start of a new learning procedure.

I'm a fighter, a grinder, a hustler. This has its advantages, but it also has its disadvantages. It's part of my personality, and it comes out when I'm coaching runners to achieve their goals. So naturally, when I was working with Mum through her recovery regiment, every single day, my coaching nature came out. I would try to push and push. But people with brain damage and neural fatigue have little to no resilience, and once they're tired, that's it. Their brains are working so hard to do everything we take for granted. It's all on a conscious level. She may have learned a new task, say, for example, sitting down and standing up—important and necessary tasks—but she would remember it for the moment and then forget it again the next day. We would have to relearn and relearn and relearn.

To give you an example of how this feels, imagine you are learning for the first time to play the piano. Everything you do at the start involves utmost concentration. You have to think so hard to remember where to put your hands next. Then after practice, you get faster and if you continue to practice it starts to become automatic. It becomes subconscious, and it's easier. You can get to a stage where you can actually play the piano and do something else at the same time, like singing or talking. You are operating from a subconscious level.

We have thousands of things as adults that are programmed into us, and we don't have to think about them with full concentration. Have you ever driven home from work, the same old route, and got home to realise that you can't even remember driving home? You did it almost on autopilot. This ability makes it so easy for us to do things without a lot of energy and focus. However, when every single part of a movement, for example, takes conscious effort, even with a healthy normal brain you will become exhausted very quickly. So, we were fighting this fatigue, along with the aftermath of the inflammation in the brain causing massive brain fog, sluggish thought processes, and completely broken links (like internet links) that no longer went anywhere.

In dire situations, many people can't see any light at the end of the tunnel, and they lose hope. They just stop. They can't see the way forward, or they can't see the immediate results, so they just give up. But as long as there is forward movement, maybe measured over months or years, that's all that matters. Like living in the daily grind or making it up the second pass in the Himalayan race, we can't necessarily see what is just around the corner. We don't know if it is going to be worth it. But I knew not doing anything would lead to disaster, loss, death. The logical action was to keep on going, even though it was painful, hard, heartbreaking, oftentimes torturous. The family and I had to believe that what we were doing was making a difference. For us, the only way we could see the progress we'd made was with the little videos I'd recorded along the way. We were so engrossed in the daily tasks that we couldn't see the bigger picture.

Due to the spasticity in some of Mum's limbs, it was very painful for her to be stretched. The version of stretching we were doing with Mum was more a case of just opening up muscles. We had no real idea of measuring if what we were doing was working. As Mum's consciousness improved, I started to see how important it had been to keep her muscles active. We had done really well at ensuring her muscles didn't atrophy to a point they were useless, as very quickly happens with people who are immobile and bedridden. As her condition improved and she began to become more mobile, she was able to make use of them.

Mum always had solid legs. Everyone teased her that even as a baby she had heavy legs. She was always self-conscious of them and only ever wore long dresses, trousers, or skirts. She had a lot of muscle mass in her legs, as well as too much fluid and fat, but her bones were big and strong too. The thickness of her knees, the actual bones, had always fascinated me. Compared to mine, they were twice the size. She hated them, but I tell you if she hadn't had such good, strong, muscular legs and heavy bones, she would likely never have walked again. Even after more than a year of hardly any moving, she still had muscle. Her bone density was still good and those reserves were coming to her aid now as she learned to move again. But one thing I hadn't bargained on was just how much both the lack of movement and the spasticity had shortened her muscles, so that she was now completely unable to bend, stretch, or reach her feet to put socks or pants on, or put her hands up past the level of her shoulders. This was to be a whole new battle that we are still fighting against: the shortness and tightness of her muscles; the loss of elasticity, and the spasticity.

From all the research I'd been conducting on therapies, rehabilitation, and the physiology of the human body, I learned that standing upright is crucial for many biological functions. Due to the force of gravity on your skeletal system, standing can help build bone density and bone strength, as well as help the brain retrain and maintain balance, and it can even affect your digestion. Gravity is actually essential for health. It also affects proprioception[10] and strength of the musculoskeletal system. Astronauts have long known that no gravity means the weakening of the muscles and bone density.

With all of that, it seemed to me that it was important for Mum's recovery that we get her up and out of the bed as soon as possible and for as long as possible. I sourced a standing machine from the hospital. It looked like a big torture device, with a crank to pump Mum up into a standing position, and with straps to hold her in place. She wasn't actually standing, because the machine was holding her up, but as far as I could tell, it would have the same effect on her body. I strapped her into that thing two or three times a day and would leave her in it for twenty minutes at a time. She hated it! But I made her do it because I was adamant that it was good for her recovery. I was sure being upright was going to help build her spatial awareness and re-develop her sense of balance or at least help her brain understand what upright and straight was.

Perhaps one of the more curious parts of her recovery was that she couldn't understand her elbows. We would

---

[10] Macquarie Dictionary definition for proprioception:
noun the perception of where one's body is and what it is doing, allowing one to perform a function without looking at what one is doing.

work on instigating a desired movement of her arm. She didn't know what straight was. If you asked her to move her arm straight out from her body, she would bend her arms. She just didn't understand the concept of her elbow. We would get her to do elbow movements which would end up looking much like a robot dance. Even to this day, she struggles with what the elbows are meant to do.

As functioning adults, it's hard to imagine any of this knowledge of our own body being undone. It's common in patients who've suffered extensive brain damage. They say once you learn to ride a bike you never forget how, but that isn't true in the case of brain damage. It was such an astounding experience to see how many of the daily functions we take for granted can be undone and how many Mum had to learn from scratch. We're so used to baby-sized humans learning to crawl, then walk and talk, so we're used to that progression. But babies have windows of learning for specific skills, and their minds are open and ready for it. As adults, we don't have the same windows of learning. The neuroplasticity is harder to achieve; that window of opportunity has passed, due to age. But we can do it with brute force. Through the power of repetition, and with a multi-pronged approach, Mum's recovery continued. We used hyperbaric oxygen therapy, nootropics[11], good food, walking frames, standing aids, parallel bars, vibration plates, foot stimulation devices, photo biomodulation lasers, peroneal nerve stimulation and we saw progress in her posture and balance.

---

[11] Macquarie Dictionary definition of nootropics:

adjective 1. of or relating to a drug which affects the brain, affording improvements in alertness, memory, etc.

For months, she couldn't initiate the movement of her legs on the walker or self-propel. All she was able to do was lean heavily on it, and if we left her, she'd just stand there, leaning on the attached frame with wheels. The only way to get her to move was for us to pull her or push her; move her legs for her. At first it took two of us, one in front of her and one behind. You might not know this, but if you pull a stroke victim along in a walker like that, their legs will move. But it isn't classed as real walking because they aren't initiating the movement. It's because their brain remembers not how not to fall, so technically they're just catching themselves from face planting, rather than moving. In the medical world, it's not considered walking because of the lack of self-initiation.

So, in this fashion, her very first steps were with that walking frame, with me and the boys pushing and pulling her. We had been using the walker since hospital, but then it was just very few steps at a time. Now we were able to include longer walking sessions to our rehabilitation schedule.

We'd let her rest, recover and then we'd try again, and slowly we built up to ten, twenty, fifty, one hundred steps. It was inch by devastating inch. We only had a small house, with an even smaller lounge room, so with nowhere else to go, we would walk Mum round and around in circles. We were constantly turning corners and dodging furniture, and I'm surprised we didn't wear a track in the carpet.

We continued around and around the lounge room for months, not seeing much improvement. We just kept up the routine, with no idea if it was working, just hoping she was learning the behaviour. Even to this day, she struggles to propel herself forward, because her calf muscles don't work like they should due to the drop foot she suffered from being bedridden for so long. Despite us now using foot braces, she has limited ankle movement. So where you and I would roll forward onto our toes and pushed off, she can't. She just sort of clumps along like you would in ski boots.

I knew from doing extreme ultramarathons that the brain goes into emergency mode when it thinks you're doing something that could kill you. In long distance running there is this thing called the central governor, which is when the brain—as an emergency response to extreme fatigue and the danger it poses—will physically stop you recruiting your muscles. That's why you often see long distance runners moving with the awkward little shuffle known as the ultramarathon shuffle. It's also called the "ugly shuffle" by those that know it well. Your brain is literally putting the brakes on to try and make you stop. It's quite amazing to think the brain actually gets to a point and says, 'this person is going to kill us if I let them continue, so I'm going to lock down the muscles so they can't use their legs properly.' But through my training, I knew I could postpone the onset of this self-defence mechanism by utilising short periods of walking and changing up the stride length and by doing very short regular stretches and resets by doing exercises such as squatting down and leg swings.

I'd learned from experience that if I stopped to walk for a few minutes every hour it would delay the onset, and I could keep pushing myself before this mechanism kicked in and stopped me using my muscles properly.

I used the same principle with Mum. It may have only been getting her up into the walker for a few steps, with us pushing and pulling her. But I gave her a rest afterward and then tried again. Initially, even just that was so tiring for Mum, that we'd have to put her back to bed for a few hours. But we continued like that for months, getting incrementally better. I called these little pauses, and still do—re-calibrating her brain. Whenever she starts to lose form, even now when walking, we stop, take three deep diaphragmatic breaths to calm the nervous system down, then we go again, and again, and again.

It felt like we were flying blind. We just didn't know if she would ever be "normal" again. I continued my research into anything I could find that I thought would help her. We were living on hope. But that hope started to morph into belief when I stumbled across an American neuroscientist named Paul Bach-y-Rita. He was known for his research on neuroplasticity and the effects of using sensory substitution devices. His story stems from the fact that his father suffered a stroke that damaged his spatial awareness and balance systems just like Mum's situation. Bach-y-Rita spent three years rehabilitating his father and teaching him how to first crawl, and then walk again. It's a beautiful story, after which Bach-y-Rita's father remarries, regains his life, and even goes back to mountain climbing. Years later, his father dies on a mountain, but doing what he loved.

The amazing part of that story is that after his death they conducted an autopsy on his brain. It was discovered that the part of his brain that usually controls walking and spatial awareness and balance, etc, was dead. It was completely gone. Yet, he was fully functioning at the time of his death. The doctors were completely stumped as to how he could walk, and the theory was, that due to neuroplasticity, other parts of his brain had compensated and taken on the job of the dead part of his brain.

It was a huge breakthrough, and I was enthralled by his other work too. I couldn't stop reading more about Bach-y-Rita. He'd also developed an electro-stimulation device that when used on the tongue, he could bypass the body's normal vestibular system and teach new ways of finding balance. If you ever want an exciting read on neuroplasticity and how we can overcome the loss of senses by feeding the information into our brains by other methods, I would highly recommend looking into Paul Bach-y-Rita. Dr Norman Doidge tells this story in his book *The Brain that Changes Itself*[2] which I also highly recommend reading. This became our bible.

Spurred on by the findings, I looked for his electro-stimulation device, thinking I could use it alongside the other treatments we were working with. But they were only available in Canada, and unfortunately, we'd have to fly Mum there because we couldn't learn remotely. It was a bit of a dead end. Travelling with Mum was impossible. Instead, I got in touch with a New Zealander, who did actually go to Canada for the device. He explained that before treatment he couldn't stand without falling over, and that during his twenty-minute sessions with the device, he could stand! After his treatment was complete, he had his balance back and happily went back to his life.

---

[2] Doidge, N. (2007). *The brain that changes itself: Stories of personal triumph from the frontiers of brain science.* New York: Viking.

I was emboldened by the discoveries despite not being able to get to Canada for this therapy. There was another type of injection therapy I discovered in Florida, US, which would also have been fantastic to try out. It was called Etanercept[13]. On *60 Minutes* they showed a piece on the reversal of a woman's stroke symptoms. I followed this up and found I would need over $50 000 to get there and would also need to stay for three weeks.

This Etanercept therapy—in layman's terms—attacks the inflammation in the brain after a stroke or aneurysm. They had miraculous and immediate recoveries from using this therapy. I hoped to get Mum there, but I didn't have the money or the ability to travel with her in her fragile state. I tried to get her onto a clinical trial in Australia, but unfortunately this was still yet to happen. I even followed up with other Kiwis who had travelled to Florida and had success. I was so sad that it couldn't be done here.

Next, I looked into stem cell therapy but hit another dead end with this. They wouldn't take her into clinical trials, either. I was constantly just looking for ways to get ahead but living in New Zealand has its unfortunate limitations. Even though I couldn't get those therapies, I used those case studies, and Dr Norman Doidge's book, as my guiding lights. I used his and other examples and research to find alternative treatments that might just work.

At the same time, I managed to get Mum back into the hospital-based physiotherapy programme. There were a few hoops to jump through to get there, but we

[13] Watch this amazing recovery in the *60 Minutes* episode on YouTube: https://www.youtube.com/watch?v=-nEtQ-Wxkas

were excited about the prospect of having professional physiotherapists to work through some exercises with Mum. In addition, there was excitement about the thought of all the equipment they had that we didn't have at home. The program ran for six weeks, with two one-and-a-half-hour long sessions a week. It was about eight months after the aneurysm, and by that stage we were getting into the walker training with Mum. We were still working through sessions of functionality exercises to keep her whole body fit and healthy. Well, as best we could. I remember sitting back to watch how the physiotherapists interacted with Mum, wondering what new techniques they'd use that I could replicate at home. I'm always looking for ways to improve what I'm doing, so the prospect of discovering more ways to help Mum recover was exciting.

I watched as the team of physiotherapists moved Mum through a series of warm-ups before taking a break. They stopped to fill out some paperwork, nodded their heads and ticked some boxes, before working through another series of warm-ups. I slowly realised they weren't warm-ups I was watching but the actual exercises. I felt like it was a baby-sitting service, especially when compared to what we'd been doing at home.

Being an athlete, I know what tired is. I live it, I breathe it, and I know when you can push and when you need to back off. When I trained with Mum, I was incredibly careful to work within the limit of her brain fatigue. I would push her right up to the edge of failure, and then take a break, recalibrate and get back into it. But the physiotherapists would do a round of exercises and say, 'Oh, now she's fatigued. Let's take a break.'

I'd been working with her for months, and I knew she only needed a small break. We often took a moment to close our eyes, control our breathing, and calm down, like a meditation, before getting back into it, again and again. But they just stopped far too early and more often than was necessary, and it was a complete waste of time.

Neither Mum nor I were particularly impressed with how the sessions ran and, because I felt they weren't pushing Mum hard enough, I couldn't really see her improving. But we did keep going because I could see how important the parallels bars were for Mum. They were far better for her to learn how to walk than the walker because they allowed her to support herself. She was learning to put one foot in front of the other by shifting her weight and moving her opposite arm forward. It was the first time she had been able to be up and moving forward without help since the aneurysm.

I know I keep referring to Mum learning how to be a human again, just like a baby does. But I did think it was amusing when they hooked Mum into this bouncing harness that was connected to the roof, just like a Jolly-Jumper. Slowly, she started to get the hang of moving her legs, whilst supporting her weight on the bars. At the end, she'd sit down to recover, and go back the other way.

Playlist Link: See the video on the lisatamati.com/ Playlist: Isobel's first steps on the parallel bars at the hospital

Over the course of the program, I asked several times if I could bring Mum up to use the parallel bars outside of the sessions. I could see the effect they were having on her walking, and I wanted to do everything I could to help her get mobile again. But they refused. They explained there was a problem with health and safety issues, because if anything happened to us while we were there, they would be liable. I found it frustrating to have the equipment right there, and to see the improvements Mum made on it, but only being allowed to use it when we were supervised.

At the end of the six weeks, there was an assessment session. All the way through they ticked boxes and talked at Mum as if she was an idiot. They conducted testing on her cognitive abilities as well as her physical abilities and assessed how well she performed and what her level of improvement was. Afterwards, we were called into a meeting with the doctors, physiotherapists, and specialists to discuss whether we should continue Mum's sessions. *Yet another bloody intimidating meeting*, I thought. I couldn't help but feel a little anxious as we walked in, wondering if it would be like the last time. This time I didn't have my brother's presence to back me up.

We sat down, and they began explaining what tests they'd carried out, why, and what they were looking for. They continued on to say Mum had failed here, here, and here, and that they'd graded her poorly everywhere: on comprehension and ability. The head doctor blurted out in front of my mother, 'She is far below the level of a severe dementia patient, and there's not much to work with and because of that we have decided to kick her out of the programme. There is nothing much we can do with her.'

I was angry. Not so much at the junior staff but at the upper echelon. I knew my Mum was intelligent. I knew she was improving. Sitting hard on my extreme anger, I just turned and looked at Mum, 'And how does that make you feel, Mum?'

She took a deep breath and released it slowly before saying, 'Well, I was feeling quite empowered before I came in here. I thought I was making great progress, but now I'm feeling very depressed. I don't know what to think, and it makes me not want to carry on.'

I looked back to the team in time to see their eyes widen in shock. They'd graded her with little-to-no comprehension and unable to communicate. They'd spoken over her, and if I was being really honest, I'd say they treated her like she was an imbecile. The tragic thing was that Mum had just been intimidated by their stupid tests. She had commented to me a few days before that she felt like she was a little kid in school again, about to get the strap for misspelling a word. All her learning anxiety had come back. So, she'd just refused to talk to them when they were working with her. She went back to feeling like that scared little girl back at school. She thought they were rude. She didn't like the way they spoke down to her. But they didn't know that. As far as they were concerned, she was *unable* to communicate more than a few words and didn't even know what town she was in or what day of the week it was.

Despite her reply showing an obvious level of intelligence and eloquence, they didn't change their judgement. We were kicked out of the programme. I gave them an "F" for fail in my personal grading system. But they were good at ticking their damn boxes.

I love to think now of just how far we have come. I often joke with Mum about her "below the level of an extreme dementia patient" diagnosis. I wonder what they would think if they ever saw Mum now. No one has ever asked me, 'How did you do it?' The ones who do still see her just nod and say keep doing what you are doing. Many are sceptical when they hear of a miraculous recovery. I have heard that from so many other people I have met on my journey who also had "miraculous" recoveries. No one wants to know why or how.

I took away what I could from the sessions I had observed. If nothing else, I had learned that we needed to get access to parallel bars. We could see that they would really make a difference in her recovery. From there on, there was one physio that we worked with privately, when we could afford it. His name is Joshua Johnson, and he specialises in neuro-physiotherapy. His knowledge and methods seemed far more advanced than what we'd seen, and I truly felt he understood the interaction between Mum's brain and body and knew ways to work with the brain damage.

The sessions were expensive, but so worth it! Not only did he work closely and respectfully with Mum, but he actually spoke to her like she was all there, and I am grateful to him for that. There was something in the way he spoke about the treatment. He spoke like we would make it and that gave me hope. I have nothing but respect for Josh and all the support he gave us along the way, not only in the sessions, but also what I learned from him. When money was tight—and it got tight—I simply tried to copy what he'd been doing with Mum. Ever so slowly, Mum was able to walk further and further with the walker, but she was still unable to stand unaided without falling over.

Chapter Sixteen
Walking!

'She's standing on her own!' We were all beaming, yahooing like parents must do when a baby takes its first steps. In a lot of ways the comparison was quite apt. She worked at her balance and pushed her walker around the room just like a little toddler human learning to walk, and finally, she was able to stand on her own. Only at seventy-five years old you don't bounce as well as a toddler does when you fall, and age and immobility are a big problem.

On this day, she had got herself to the edge of the bed, swung her legs over, and then, with her calves supported against the side of the bed, she stood up on her own. It was a massive milestone for us: one that filled us with enthusiasm and optimism to continue doing what we were doing. To do that complicated movement requires so many things to be working in your head. We were making progress, and after months of repeating the same exercises, we could see the work was paying off.

I decided I had to get Mum parallel bars. I'd seen how much they helped and how they were the next step in her progression after the walker. I knew, if we could access some, it would help turn Mum's ability to now stand without one of us holding her, into walking again. In true twenty-first century style, I put a post on social media explaining our need for the bars, and fully expected that if we were going to buy them, it would cost thousands of dollars to get them installed. A lovely lady woman named Amy Roper reached out and explained they'd been given a set to help her father recover after he'd had a stroke, but sadly he'd passed away. When I asked her how much they were, she said she wanted to donate them because they had been donated to her: she was paying it forward. They were donating this equipment to us to help Mum recover and it was worth a lot of money. I was so incredibly grateful, as I had an inkling of how important these would be in Mum's recovery.

There were a few points along the recovery journey where we seemed to take one big leap and getting the parallels bars was certainly one of them. Having them at home meant we could practice her walking every single day. And not just the walking, but also a whole list of other movement and balance exercises as well. Think of her like a ballerina doing barre work and balancing on one leg, and doing leg rises, all with the support of the bars beside her.

Every day we'd work on her balance and strength with those bars, and finally it started to pay off. I came home one day, and my brother said that Mum had just taken her first steps without holding onto the bars. I grabbed my camera and started filming as Mum got back between the bars and showed us what she could do. It was a tremendous achievement, and it was quite soon after she'd stood for the first time.

Playlist Link: Here's all of us proudly watching as Mum takes her first few steps unaided. See lisatamati.com/playlist: Mum standing first time.

I have a short video clip I took of Mum walking in between her parallel bars. To come from not even being able to sit straight, or to find her mouth to put food in it, or even to pushing a button with her hand, to being able to walk unaided, a half dozen steps was simply amazing. The brain retraining and recuperation required to achieve such a feat is nothing short of monumental. It was the first time in the whole journey when I really thought we are going to do this, it can be done, and we will get there. Up until that point it had been blind faith, utter bloody-minded stubbornness and pure hope that had got me through. Now I knew it was indeed not just an impossible fantasy but actually achievable. It felt like we were really picking up speed with her recovery. We were all excited about the idea of her not being confined to a wheelchair and being able to move around the house unaided.

Playlist Link: See lisatamati.com/playlist: Isobel walks unaided on parallel bars for the first time.

It was shortly after that when I was in contact with a friend named Murray Dick, who has been a tremendous supporter of some of the crazy things I'd been up to over the years. He sponsored me running in the Death Valley race; a 217km nonstop race through the hottest desert on earth, with temperatures up to 57 degrees celsius, and he was also part of my crew. Then again when I ran

2 250km through NZ for CanTeen and Curekids—two NZ charities—he was there backing me financially in 2009. He was a huge mentor and role model for me, not to mention the best sponsor an athlete could have. Through him supporting my ventures over the years, he had come to know Mum. When she was in hospital, he made a point of coming to visit her and checking we were okay. It was during one of those visits, he said that if there was anything he, or his engineering company could do, that all I had to do was ask. So, I did.

I asked if he could build a metal handrail that would be a continuation of the parallel bars that went right around the garden. With the success of the parallel bars, my idea was that we could get Mum outside in the garden, with nature and the sunshine, and at the same time, she would have to walk up and down the stairs, over stones, grass and even through the garden. It was like an obstacle course for Mum.

Murray thought it was a fantastic idea, and donated his time, money, and his employee's work time to produce this wonderful handrail that wrapped all around our yard. And we made daily use of it. It enabled Mum to develop her balance, and concentrate on where she was putting her feet, and the more she used it the stronger she got. She was now okay just walking with one hand on the rail or using it for strength and mobility exercises. From squats to stretching, we did it all on here.

We used the handrail 4-5 times a day, and I was absolutely relentless in pushing her. I felt like a drill master:

Forward.

Backwards.

Now sideways.

Stop.

Take giant steps.

Do a squat.

Balance on one leg.

Her recovery really began to move ahead, and soon she was able to move with only one hand on the bar, and then none. Though we were always there to catch her if she fell. Mum wore a big belt that we used to just stabilise her and grab her if she tipped over. This gave us a bit of security while at the same time we were intentionally weaning her off all the supports, one by one. When she did start walking unaided, she struggled with her balance. Due to the stroke she suffered on the right side of her body, she walked robotically. It was like she had no concept of left and right, as she'd try to move her left leg and her left arm at the same time, and then her right leg and right arm. I had to try to retrain her brain into using the opposite hand and opposite leg.

I spoke to the guy who had gone to Canada to try out Bach-y-Rita's balance device using the tongue stimulation, and he had mentioned how important Nordic walking sticks were. They forced you to use the arms in unison with the legs. The idea was that it would teach her to swing her left and right arms when she was walking, at the correct time. And it did help. But to this day, it remains a battle once she gets tired. Another thing she really struggled with was anything that required turning. That is a whole new level of difficulty. And she couldn't turn when she was walking! She would stop, and sort of wobble on the spot as she shuffled her feet around to a different direction. All these intermittent advancements were required to get to a level of what we call normal walking.

I remember getting so frustrated with her brain, not her but the brain damage. I would sometimes let the frustration out in my voice. It was entirely unhelpful to her. I found myself getting annoyed at, what seemed at times, to be a lack of progression. I would direct her through a movement, and think, *Why can't you do this? It's really not that hard.* But I would have to stop and remind myself that her brain was working overtime. We take for granted the movement of lifting our leg. It's as simple as just doing it. But for someone who has suffered severe brain damage it's not that easy. They have to consciously think about how to shift their weight, what to grab onto, how to grab it, how to tense their muscles, and how to move their leg off the ground. They have to consciously concentrate on every little tiny movement that we would just do without thinking.

There was one time when my frustration must have been coming through in my voice (I am known as the "Fun Police" for a reason). I was directing Mum through an exercise and was probably annoying her, 'Come on, Mum, do it. Pick up your leg. Concentrate. Come on, you can do it. Just pick it up.' Sergeant Major Lisa can be quite a bitch.

Then all of a sudden she snapped back, 'Stop yelling at me!'

I am ashamed to admit it, but it was bullying led by frustration. It stemmed from the thousands of hours we had been working. It wore me down, and so too was it wearing Mum down. It's hard to imagine what it would have been like for her to have to learn how to be a functioning adult again. The thousands of hours trapped inside a body that refused to do what she wanted it to. In those moments, I'm glad we can laugh, because humour played a large role in the journey after the aneurysm. I think the ability to make a joke about something that otherwise would be serious, tedious, and mind-blowingly frustrating gave us the chance to vent our emotions in a way that created a positive environment for Mum, particularly when we had a debrief afterwards. I discovered whenever I lost the plot and got grumpy at her, her brain would go into 'numpty' mode, and she was unable to perform. To this day, any stress from outside will hinder her performance. It's like her brain can't deal with too many things at the same time. So, I have learned no matter how impatient or frustrated I am, I must keep it together for her sake or ruin her ability to concentrate and get better. There are definitely times when I couldn't keep it together and every one of those times I hated myself. But I got on with it and let it go quickly because guilt is a useless emotion. I just tried to do better the next time.

I have another video I took one night of Mum standing in the kitchen leaning on the bench getting crackers out and feeding herself. A moment later, Dad came in and wrapped his big hands around her to make sure she didn't fall. The two of them were munching on crackers and having a giggle. In that moment, I was as happy as I have ever been. My two parents together, holding each other, supporting each other, having a feed together, happy. There were many times on this journey where I pictured Dad alone without Mum, and it was devastating. Dad, throughout this whole journey, has always been there for her, always looked after her, having to learn everything that Mum had previously done for him. It was one of the most joyous things in the world for me to see. Mum standing, eating on her own, and enjoying her food again with her husband. Considering the years of work we put in, it was such an achievement.

Play List Link: See lisatamati.com/playlist: Mum learning to eat and stand by herself in the kitchen

---

Chapter Seventeen
Sam's Story

My day-to-day life was so different to what it had been before the aneurysm. Before, Mum and I had a retail shop in New Plymouth. I would make the jewellery and Mum ran it day to day. We also ran an online jewellery ecommerce store. I ran several businesses that needed my total daily input. I do corporate motivational speaking all over the country, a podcast called Pushing the Limits[14] and an online run coaching company that trains hundreds of athletes from all around the world, alongside my business partner Neil Wagstaff and some part-time employees. We also facilitate running retreats, and I co-owned the southern hemispheres toughest 100-mile mountain ultra-marathon, The Northburn100[15]. I had been working hard on building my brand with a tonne of content on social media as well as doing influencer work and work for my sponsors. My life had been absolutely, manically busy. It turns out, I had no idea what busy was.

Following Mum's aneurysm, my income had dropped dramatically. With Mum improving, I was able to start putting more time back into my work commitments

---

[14] See a list of my podcasts on: https://www.lisatamati.com/page/podcast/
[15] www.northburn100.co.nz

while still retaining a training schedule with Mum. My typical day would be: wake up early, work for an hour, head to Mum's and work with her all day on various aspects of her recovery (feeding her the right food, supplements, etc.) and then coming over after tea, training, cooking dinner, then working until 1:00am in the morning. Rinse and repeat. This sort of daily grind became my new normal, but I was burning the candle at both ends. My health was beginning to suffer. I was living on adrenaline and sheer willpower, and my body was no longer young. I was burning out. However, life was about to set me up for another adventure that would teach me more about the preciousness of life.

A year prior to Mum's aneurysm, I had been doing a speaking tour of the North Island put on by one of my sponsors. One night, I was at the Century Theatre in Napier where I was speaking to five hundred people. I was on stage talking and here was this guy, right in the front row in a wheelchair. He was smiling up at me, nodding. My focus kept darting towards him. There was something about him that made me want to say hello. I am always fascinated by people's stories, and this guy just looked like he had a story to tell. So, I made a point of meeting him afterward, and I got to hear his story.

Samuel Gibson was born with brittle bone disease also known as Osteogenesis Imperfecta. His parents didn't know until he was born but refused to let that be a reason to give up on him. They loved him, cared for him and made sure he wouldn't miss out on anything life had to offer. They had tried to give Sam as close to a normal life as possible. They had obviously brought him up as an incredibly resilient and no holds barred type of man who wouldn't let his disability stop him living his life to the full. I was amazed, just listening to his story.

He'd designed and built a wheelchair that enabled him to be up high one minute then would take him right down to ground level the next. Sam had lived an incredible life, even backpacking around Asia. This wheelchair he had invented was like an all-terrain vehicle that could go anywhere, and he'd gone on to establish a company that sold his wheelchair all around the world. He happily continued to tell me that he'd actually met the love of his life whilst backpacking. Her name was Jen. She was Canadian. They had fallen in love, married, and then decided they wanted to have children.

Now the thing with Osteogenesis Imperfecta is that it's hereditary. If Sam and Jen were to have children, it was highly likely that they too would be affected. Sam spent eight years learning all he could about the disease and even worked closely with geneticists. He was adamant that he wanted to have children with his wife but didn't want to pass on his disease. And can you believe it … he did it! Jen gave birth to two healthy girls who incidentally ended up going to school with the children of Neil. Sam's can-do attitude, his drive, and zest for life was infectious, and I wanted to get to know this guy more. I love gutsy people like Sam. This man, all three feet of him, found solutions to help him fulfil his dreams. His story was all about facing adversity, overcoming obstacles, and not giving up.

We said our goodbyes, and before I turned to leave, he said, 'If you ever want a little guy rolling beside you whilst you are running something epic somewhere, then I am your guy.'

As I left the event that night, I couldn't stop thinking about what he'd said. *Was he for real? Did he mean it?* He sure as hell seemed to be serious. The more I thought about it, the more I thought, *Why the hell not?*

I reconnected with him over social media, and together we started to plan out "something epic." We mulled over a number of ideas for a while and then we stumbled upon a trail that we thought would be cool to do. The trail is called the Alps2Ocean[16]. It traverses 330kms from the base of Mount Cook to the ocean. The scenery is epic; the distance is epic. Working out how we could logistically do it was something extraordinarily difficult. But we liked the challenge, so we set to it. We would need a crew. We would need equipment, and we would need to do this for a cause. We would need sponsors and ways to raise money. I had done this type of thing before and made a number of mistakes along the way, so I knew just what would be required.

As the plan began to take shape, we found a wonderful reason for our run. Little Ryuki is a boy from Christchurch who had been born with the same disease as Sam. The money we would raise would go towards supporting Ryuki and providing him with the equipment to lead a life full of joy and adventure just like Sam had, despite his debilitating disease. There would be a team of us running: Haisley, my business partner Neil, Sam, and I. The idea was brilliant, and we were all so excited. For me, running an event just for the sake of it had lost its shine, but doing one to help someone else

---

[16] See: https://www.alps2ocean.com/

made sense and helped me stay focused and determined. Months went by, and we made inroads into all the work that had to be done.

Then when Mum got sick everything was stuck on hold. Sam was still training hard and preparing for the event. He had to be fit enough to withstand the rigours of travel, of rolling through rough terrain for hours and hours on end. Neil, who is an exercise scientist and gym owner, started training Sam. He rocked up to the gym a number of times a week, and Neil would put him through his paces. Designing a plan to work around his severe disabilities, Neil had to be so careful with him. Even lifting a small weight could break a bone. Sam had broken hundreds of bones in his life. In fact, just being born had seen his hips fracture. But delicate and fragile as he was, he could still benefit from being fit. Neil studied his condition and worked with him to get him strong, and he was making great progress. Neil and Sam would do events or training runs/rolls together on the weekends, too. Then tragedy struck.

I was at home training Mum when I got the phone call from Neil. He was beyond devastated. He and Sam were doing an event together, and Neil had been a few steps in front of Sam when it happened. The event was the Hawkes Bay Half Marathon, and it was to be a training event for our big run. Sam's wheelchair had a catastrophic failure. It threw him to the ground, where he sustained massive head injuries. A cold dread set in my stomach. It was too soon after Mum's aneurysm. I could feel the same emotions bubbling back to the surface. Sam was taken straight to hospital in a critical condition. The local hospital didn't have the facilities to help him, so to give him the best chance the doctors were discussing the option of flying him to Wellington. It was just like Mum, and I hoped beyond hope Sam would make it.

Sam's condition deteriorated rapidly, and the doctors soon realised there was no hope. They made the call not to transfer him to Wellington. Sadly, Sam died the next day. I was shell-shocked. I felt devastated, and I felt guilty. If he hadn't met me, if we hadn't planned this epic adventure, if he hadn't been training for it, if he hadn't been at that half marathon that day, he would still be alive. It was stupid and irrational, but I felt I was responsible in some roundabout way. He was the CFO of his company. He'd backpacked around the world in a wheelchair. He'd yachted across the Cook Straits solo. He'd spent the best part of a decade researching the right way to father two beautiful children free of his disease. He was so inspirational, and I couldn't help but feel if he hadn't met me then he would still be alive. The guilt haunted me. Rationally, I knew I was being silly and that he wouldn't have wanted me to think like that. But irrationally, the wounds of Mum's time in hospital, and her brush with death were still so raw. I couldn't stop thinking how unkind fate is. *Why do some live and others don't?*

In the horrible aftermath of Sam's death, we decided we had to do something to honour him. Like everything else in our journey after the aneurysm, I knew we couldn't stop. We couldn't let little Ryuki down. We'd committed ourselves to raising money for him, and now we had to honour Sam as well. Sam would have wanted us to keep going. We decided to change the plan and to run from where Sam was born in Hawera, right across the North Island to Havelock North, where he had been living with his family. We were going to raise money for little Ryuki, and at the same time honour Sam and all the amazing things he'd achieved in his life, against all odds.

Shortly after I'd locked in the idea, I was talking to Mum about what had happened. Her speech was continuing to improve. I loved and cherished just being able to talk to her again. She knew Sam and admired him so much, and we talked about how unfair it was that Sam had died. It felt like I was talking to the old Mum again. I told Mum about our new plan to run across the North Island instead of doing the Alps2Ocean trail. I was so excited about it but so worried what I would do with Mum as she needed me every day. She was still in a wheelchair at that time and totally dependent, and unable to move very much.

Now, Mum has crewed for me at dozens of races. She drove the car behind me for forty-two days when I ran through New Zealand, and she just loved being a part of my adventures. She looked at me with tears in her eyes and said, 'I won't ever be able to crew for you again, will I?'

In that moment I was both hit emotionally by that fact, followed quickly by a determination that she would crew for me again. I had no idea how the hell I would make that happen, but I promised her there and then that she would be with me, that she would indeed be crewing me on this adventure too.

The logistics of having someone so fragile with us as we ran across the North Island was daunting, and I knew she would physically suffer. I wouldn't be able to train her for those six days we were away. Sometimes having a goal is even more important than routine. It's a reason to fight, a reason to get better and have something to look forward to. It was a chance for her to feel like she was still a valuable part of a project. This was more important than the few days of training she would miss, and I would work hard to mitigate that and include as much movement as possible. The load would be on both her body and on us, as we ran all day and had to look after her around that. But I hugged my Mum and said, 'Yes, you are coming, and this is going to be epic.'

She was, and still is, my biggest supporter, and I didn't want to do this without her. I knew in that moment that Sam was smiling down at us too. The whole point of this expedition, and for starting the Samuel Gibson Memorial Trust, was to enable people with disabilities to live full lives. Having Mum do her own challenge and be part of the team was doing just that, enabling someone less able to live fully. I watched as her face lit up at the thought. I could see what she was thinking. Finally, after eight months of being bedridden and wheeled around in a chair, she was going to get back out there. I didn't know how or when I was going to make it happen, and I didn't care. All I knew was that I now had a new goal for Mum. She was going to crew for me again!

So many people—friends, professionals, and family—said we wouldn't be able to do it. But when had their opinions stopped us? I knew it was going to be a massive toll on her body. The event itself was only a short one, with three days of preparation and another three running. But I knew it was the lack of training and sitting in the car that would be a problem. But I believed in her, and sometimes that's all you need. The event was going to be a huge break away from home. Even just the travel in the car would be taxing for her, with all the vibrations, and noise, and images flashing past. With her brain still adjusting, it could be a sensory and physical overload that could exhaust her. Ten months had passed, and she was getting stronger. Sometimes the mental health of the person has to also be taken into consideration. I knew what it would mean for her to just live her life again, to remind her what her life was like. I took a calculated risk.

My biggest problem was finding someone to be her dedicated caregiver during the run, who could drive her in the van and who was capable of being solely responsible for her during the hours I was running, including helping her at night. I struck it lucky with our next-door neighbour, Kirsty Calder. She is an experienced caregiver, and she volunteered to help. It was a huge ask. It's one thing to care for someone at Mum's level of care for a few hours; it's another to be solely responsible. Without Kirsty, I honestly believe the whole thing could not have happened, and she did it because she wanted to make a difference. Even with Kirsty's help, getting everything organised for the event was no small feat.

We already bought a van with a wheelchair lift at the back, just so Mum could get around. That was one box ticked. I used whatever spare time Kirsty could give us to get back into the swing of my own training. I'd been so focused on Mum's recovery over the ten months leading up to that point, that I hadn't trained at all for any long distance running. I would squeeze in a max of thirty minutes high intensity training a day at the gym, but I certainly hadn't done hours and hours of plodding that was required to do this. I secretly expected my body to handle it. After all, I had spent twenty-four odd years doing this stuff, surely muscle memory and the years of training would still be in my legs and my body would know what to do? Man, was I wrong! I knew it was going to be difficult, but I had underestimated just how much my training had changed and how my fitness had changed. I was still very fit but in a different way, and I had sacrificed endurance for more mobility, speed, and strength. As the last few weeks before the event rolled past, I still never got more than an hour to train. I stood on the starting line, at the house where Sam was born, already completely exhausted. I was about to tip my body over the edge.

We'd committed to running 55km each day to get across the country, which in my heyday I would have done in my sleep but now that was a different ball game. I went into this thinking, *Well, I haven't trained long distance for a year, but she'll be right.* Instead of all of us running together, we would run a relay, with Haisley and I running our kms and then Neil doing his on his own.

On day one we begin at 6:00am and I was out running with Haisley, with 57km being the target. About 40km in, I could hardly run. We were down to a walk, run, walk, run. I wasn't feeling right in my body. I pushed on but really wondered how I would go. Haisley was off the back of an ultramarathon, so he was fit. He bounded along, and I was pissed off.

We met through running coaching. He had reached out to me on Facebook because he was doing a 27km run in full level 2 fireman's gear with breathing apparatus. He wanted tips on how to run in extreme heat. That's how we met and then subsequently fell in love. On our very first date we ran a 50km run together and I thought, *If he can run 50km and still perform in the bedroom after, he's a keeper.* He did. So, I married him. But now the tables had turned. The student had now surpassed the teacher. This pissed the me off in a way only a husband can. I was very glad to see the end of day one.

Neil took on the next lap on the afternoon of that first day. Despite being very fit and strong, he hadn't had much time to train. Having three children under five and running two businesses will do that to you. It took a while for him to come in that day. There was quite a bit of puking on the side of the road. So, the two top running coaches really got whipped. However, we were very moved by this cause, and we knew we had to do this to honour our friend, fit for the race or not.

On the second night, we were having dinner. We heard that Trump had just won the presidency. You know those moments were you vividly remember where you were at the time? We were thrown into a spin, thinking world war three was on the horizon. We just couldn't believe it. We kept on running.

It was not only the run itself, but also the huge amount of organisation behind it. It was exhausting, and not just for me, for all of us—crew included—and of course, Mum. She was so excited to be travelling again and on the road with us.

You never remember the hard stuff so much; you only really remember the epic moments you had. The elation at finishing, the people you met on the way, the huge amount of money you raised, the gala night at the end to raise money, and the good bits. I knew Sam would have loved that attitude because he embodied it. I'd probably bitten off more than I could chew in trying to pull it all off again, but I survived and so did Mum, with a smile on her face. She didn't get the activity she needed during the day so as soon as I stopped running, I would do my training routines with her as best I could.

After three very hard days on busy and dangerous roads, with a few close shaves, we made it to Havelock North. About 3kms out of town, we were to meet up with a bunch of supporters, kids from Samuel's girls' school, and all our crew. Neil had run the last leg up to that point, so we were all waiting for him as he trotted in, looking buggered but happy. We had literally hundreds of people there, a dozen in wheelchairs, including Mum, of course, and little Ryuki and his Mum, tonnes of kids and no police escort to bring us the last kilometres into town. The police had promised to be there to escort us but didn't turn up. So Haisley and I and a few of the crew had a hell of a job keeping everyone safe. The television crews and media were there too, and the kids thought it was a great hoot running into town, but I was having fits trying to make sure no one got hurt. Despite the chaos, everything worked out. The cars gave us a wide berth, and we ran with little Ryuki, my Mum, and Samuel's friends and family to the finish line. It was an epic last couple of kms. We arrived at the school where Samuel's kids went, to a huge celebration, music, food, a great big party. There were speeches and lots of photos.

Playlist Link: Running for charity across the North Island of New Zealand – 340km

---

Afterwards reporters from Seven Sharp, the daily news show here, met us in New Zealand. They asked us all about why we were doing the event and what we were raising the money for. The reporters did a wonderful job of putting a story together that paid homage to Sam and his legacy. As the camera operator moved through the crew, getting little video snippets from each of them about what the event had meant to them, they turned the lens on Mum. Now, before the aneurysm Mum hated cameras. She hated being in front of them, and she hated having her picture taken. But, as I watched, she did her best to sit a little straighter in the chair and smiled as she spoke to the camera, 'It's so inspirational what these guys have done.'

It had only been months before that Mum had still been unconscious in bed, and here she was talking on national television. Okay, it was only a few words, but I was so damned proud that she was here to share the moment and was strong enough to let them interview her. I couldn't have been more proud of her or of what she had achieved.

Sam's death had impacted us so greatly, and I still felt partly responsible. His parents and friends had come along the journey with us. We spent what little down time we had reminiscing about all the things Sam had achieved in his life, despite his disease and what the professionals said he'd be able to do. Sam's friends and family had started a trust in his name, one dedicated to helping people with disabilities live full lives. We used this running event to kick-start the trust. It was inspiring, and such a perfect way to honour what Sam was all about.

The next night the team had organised a gala auction dinner to raise money. It was held at the beautiful Craggy Range Winery. So many companies donated items for the auction. The gala was another huge mission to organise, and we were exhausted from the run, but this was the crucial part of the event, the time when money flows in. We had over a hundred attending, and I was the speaker for the evening. It was an emotional speech, being surrounded by my good friends, Sam's family, and my Mum. It was one of those nights you will never forget. Sam taught me that it didn't matter what life threw at you, you can still make the most of it, and I made sure everyone there knew how much he'd impacted my own life in the very short time I'd known him.

It was a wonderful night, and by the end we had raised $55 000 to help people with disabilities live fuller lives. I was so bone-achingly tired by the end of it all. My adrenals and my hormones were at busting point. As we left the event, I thought about everything we'd achieved. I was so happy with Mum. It was the first time since the aneurysm that she had given herself a goal to work towards, and she'd achieved it. It was a sign of her fight coming back. She'd crewed for us from a wheelchair as we crossed the country. We proved that if we wanted it to happen, then we could make it happen. However, the event had taken more out of me than I realised.

Chapter Eighteen
Time for a Wedding

Although we were so sad, we had lost our friend Samuel, truly one of the most inspiring human beings I have ever met, we were glad to be a part of Sam's legacy. Helping to empower those with disabilities was important to me. We noticed the fluidity in Mum's speech had really picked up, and her crewing adventure had ignited a spark in her and made her believe she could still be a part of real life and experience things. It became a high priority for me, and still is to this day, to make sure she has as many experiences as possible.

A week after running across the North Island something felt wrong with my body. I had a pain steadily growing in my abdomen, and I started having complications with my monthly cycle. One night, I started having incredible pains. I'd actually had a psyllium husk health drink, full of fibre, and I thought that might have had something to do with it. But as the pain intensified, I knew it couldn't be just a bowel problem. I didn't know at the time what was wrong. So many thoughts plagued my mind: *Was it just the toll of stress, sleep deprivation and exhaustion from the past ten months that was starting to catch up with me? Or something else?*

I was about to head into a very dark hole with my health. The pain and extreme cramping increased until I couldn't cope anymore. In fact, the pain was so bad I passed out. The blood loss was huge, and so we called for an ambulance to rush me to hospital. The doctors had no idea what was wrong with me. They ran some tests that came back inconclusive, and they administered morphine for the pain. After spending a day in the hospital, the pain disappeared with the morphine. Not being one to lay around, I got up and back into life. However, the bleeding got worse, much worse. My monthly cycle was totally mucked up anyway, but this was ridiculous. To make matters worse, this was only days before I married Haisley.

Our wedding had originally been planned for the February after Mum's aneurysm. So naturally, Haisley and I postponed it. I was acutely aware I didn't want to marry without Mum being at the wedding, nor did I want her to not remember it. By the time we were ready, nine months had passed. As we began planning the day, I secretly hoped that we could have Mum to the point that she could walk me down the aisle. But as we got closer to the day, Mum just wasn't there yet. She was making great progress with her parallel bars, but she wasn't at all at the point where she could walk unaided. I was resigned to the fact she would have to accompany me up the aisle in the wheelchair. I liked having little goals like this to aim for. It made her work hard, trying to get to that point, but sometimes you miss your goals. However, you're that little bit closer to the end goal having tried so hard. At least she was going to be there with me and was enjoying all the organisation of the wedding and was fully involved with it all. It's one of those lovely mother-daughter things. Mums want their daughters to have a lovely wedding and she loved it all.

So, my beautiful wedding day finally arrived. Mum was there holding my hand, wheeling beside me. Mum loved every second of it. It was a poignant moment for me. I thought about all the prognoses we had received over those nine months. I reflected on how the social worker had told us she wouldn't be here very long. How he advised us not to resuscitate if anything happened, to just let her die. I thought about the doctors saying she was never going to have a quality of life again, never going to be my intelligent, loving mum again, that she was just too old to recover from such devastating brain damage. But here she was right beside me. Life was still tough, but she was living it and enjoying it.

This day was exactly what our family needed. It was a celebration of love and family amidst the chaos of the last year. With the big event, the family had a chance to relax, eat and be merry. We forgot the hell we had all been through. It was both a wedding celebration and a celebration of life and our family still being whole. It was special having her there. It filled me with joy and pride to see my brothers picking her up from the wheelchair and dancing with her around the room. We spent much of the night like that, taking it in turns to hold Mum up and just dance with her.

PlayList Link: See lisatamati.com/playlist: Isobel and the boys dancing at the Lisa's wedding

But unbeknownst to my family, my abdominal pains had returned with a vengeance. It had been about a week since I was in hospital, and I hadn't felt anything until the day of my wedding. Typical! I swallowed painkillers (something I hate doing) and drank my bubbly and was determined to ignore it. To my horror, I looked down to see blood on my wedding dress. Can you imagine the blood on the white of the dress? Horrified, I rushed to the bathroom so determined to not let something like this ruin my wedding day. As my wonderful bridesmaids guarded the door, they helped me strip and clean the dress, before redressing me and sending me back out to the party. We went through this drama *four times* during the celebration. Thank goodness the trouble had waited until the party, not during the ceremony. I redressed, put on a smile and was determined to pretend that nothing was happening. Nothing was going to wreck my special day. I had just married the love of my life. I was focused on him and the blessings I had. The trouble could wait until tomorrow.

The fact that I spent more moments cleaning up in the bathroom throughout the night didn't matter. My bridesmaids and I would alternate between bathroom trips and the dance floor that night. In fact, despite a bit of pain, we actually managed to find the funny side. It's these moments where you really appreciate your friendships and the closeness that comes from women looking after each other. I have to take a moment to thank my bridesmaids for their help that night: Cushla, Kimberley, Nadene, and Nic—I can never thank you enough. You enabled me to have a beautiful night.

Unfortunately, that day kick-started a whole year of hell, but with my health rather than Mum's. I experienced more and more of the same attacks and their frequency increased. At its worst, I was suffering one every week. I was bleeding the entire time. Fantastic for a newly married couple, right! My poor husband got the short end of the deal and must have thought, *What the hell have I done?* After two months of solid bleeding, I was running out of blood, and I knew something was gravely wrong. The bleeding ended up going on for an entire year straight without stopping. The pain attacks I had would come on suddenly and were very similar to childbirth, except the contractions didn't stop. It was hell. I really couldn't stand the pain. My whole body would convulse, and, in those moments, I just wanted nothing more than for it to stop at whatever cost. I knew the only thing that would stop it was morphine, and that is hard to get even when you are in hospital. Emergency rushes to the hospital became the norm and every time it was a horrific experience, left in agony for hours at a time before a doctor would finally come and administer morphine.

It took months to diagnose properly what was going on and all the while the attacks were increasing in severity. At its zenith, I could hardly function but gritted my teeth and did what I could. I just didn't have enough blood in my body. Every time I stood up it would take me a minute to get my balance back as my blood pressure was so low. On one occasion, I couldn't lift my head off the pillow and would have to crawl—head low to the floor—to the toilet. Most of the time I could at least move around and function, though, but it was extremely exhausting. I had been an athlete all my life, running races for days on end, and now I could hardly walk to the letterbox. Every attack would take a couple of days to recover from, and all the while, I was still trying to work and look after Mum, seven days a week.

I was studying furiously, trying to work out what was wrong with me. By now we knew it was something to do with fibroids (benign tumours in my uterus, and adenomyosis, a type of endometriosis) that was causing the trouble.

One particularly bad attack occurred when I was in Dunedin for a speaking engagement. I had bought my husband with me, which I didn't usually do. I knew that at any time I could go down, and I did. It happened this time as I was about to board the plane home. In the fifteen minutes before take-off, I went from fine to agony, and the bleeding went mad. I took the over-the-counter painkillers I had. They wouldn't give me anything nearly strong enough to stop the pain outside of the hospital walls, so I took the pills. They did nothing. It was likely the worst flight I've ever been on in my life. I feel so sorry for my husband, who patiently sat next to me as I crushed his hands in an attempt to distract myself from the pain. By the end of the flight, I was completely unable to control myself. I was vomiting, convulsing, and struggling to breathe.

We went straight to the hospital and, finally, I got a really good doctor. Dr Ventresca did an exam and discovered the actual problem. One of the tumours—a pedunculated fibroid, the biggest of them at about the size of a grapefruit—had collapsed into the cervix. My body was desperately trying to birth this thing, but it was still attached to the wall of the uterus. I had, that very week before, sent my MRI to a specialist in Christchurch and paid to speak to him on the phone.

He too suspected that this one fibroid was the problem and now it was confirmed.

Amid all the chaos of Mum's recovery, my husband and I had been trying for a child. In fact, we had been trying for five years. Our own little baby we could raise together and love was something we both were looking forward to. I had been to the fertility specialists and had been told at the very beginning of our journey that I was too old and that I had fibroids. They said I would never be able to have a child—with IVF or without it. Promptly six weeks later I fell pregnant. Unfortunately, we lost our little one along the way, with a miscarriage at twelve weeks. We were desperately holding onto hope that we could bring a child into the world. But those dreams were shattered.

When I had the new MRI, the doctors told me I had six tumours on the inside and the outside of the uterus. They were benign, thank heavens! But they were causing havoc. My heart sunk. According to their diagnosis, my only option was to have a hysterectomy. After everything we had been through, our dreams of having a child together were in jeopardy. I outright refused. I remember, despite all the attacks I was having and the pain and the years of failing to get pregnant, I was in the doctor's office and she said point blank, 'You have to have a hysterectomy or die. Your body can't sustain this blood loss.'

Now you might already have realised, but I don't give up easily. I spent months looking for every other way. I had sought out the world's leading integrated medical practitioners. I had hair tissue mineral analysis and worked out I had damaged my kidneys from all the running I had done. I discovered my hormones were recycling. I had adrenal burnout (surprise, surprise), my thyroid wasn't operating optimally, and I wasn't processing electrolytes in the right manner. I did research on what the contraceptive pill does to a woman's body and was horrified. I discovered possible ways food and supplements could help reduce the size of the fibroids. I found out that if I could make it to menopause, the problem would go away of its own accord due to the drop in estrogen levels that was feeding the tumour growth. I found out I had estrogen dominance and sought out counsel from hormone experts from America. I even decided never to run long distances again. I didn't want to end up on dialysis, for starters, and I was heading that way. Eventually, once I discovered what worked, my overall health improved, but it took time.

Once again, it was about taking an integrated system-wide approach to the situation rather than the easy option of taking this pill. I don't believe that type of linear thinking really produces long-term results. I'd been through nearly a year of being told what the professionals thought Mum could and couldn't do, and by then we'd done a fantastic job of proving them wrong. So, I wasn't about to just take their word for it in regard to my health. I held onto hope that there was some way for me to get around having a hysterectomy. I even watched hysterectomy operations on YouTube. *Hell no! I am not having that done.*

I don't believe in burying my head in the sand but in facing the situation head on. I reached out to an old friend who is a functional nutritionist, a rehabilitation specialist, and elite athlete, Gary Moller. He works with athletes and spent his career learning how the human body reacts under the extreme pressure athletes work with. I explained the test results, and he told me I fried my body and created some serious damage. It was his belief that my kidneys weren't functioning, so the hormones weren't recycling properly which was causing tumours to grow in my uterus. Well, that was his theory anyway, but it sounded logical to me and gave me a direction to focus my research.

I was in hospital for the umpteenth time. Dr Ventresca reconfirmed the diagnosis of the Christchurch doctor. The fibroid had fallen into the cervix meaning the blood was just pouring out. Still, no one gave me the option of surgery of just that one fibroid, but I started pushing for that rather than a hysterectomy. I'd trusted my gut before, and I was driven by hope. I wanted the ability to give my husband a child, so we could conceive, birth, and raise a child together. I wasn't going to be able to do that if I didn't have a uterus. Perhaps this may sound unrealistic. By this time I was forty-eight years old. But I wanted a shot at beating the odds. I filled my mind with positive stories of women who had achieved pregnancy late in life.

Certainly my bloody mindedness can be both a weakness and a curse. But for me, I believed there was another way. I wasn't going to stop until there was really *no* other way. With this new direction, I selfishly used my podcast as a way to get some advice from experts in the fields. I contacted a hormone scholar and asked her to be a guest on my show. Dr Lindsey Berkson is an incredible doctor. She has written twenty-one books on hormones and health and is someone who has beaten many odds herself, overcoming multiple cancers and the removal of nine organs. Based on what I had heard from her own podcast, I felt her to be a kindred spirit, someone who thought outside the box when looking for answers. Her insights were invaluable. She really helped me see there could be another way other than a full hysterectomy. I was willing to do the work required; I listened to her and took action to get my health back on track. With her help, I found other experts on the subject and learned more and more about the body: its hormones, thyroid, adrenal issues, heavy metal poisoning, gut health, and so on and on.

When I had spoken with the doctor in Christchurch from the Oxford Women's Health Clinic, he had looked at my MRI results and said I had a tumour the size of a grapefruit right in the middle of my uterus. He said it was taking up all this space and thought it must have been the one that was giving me the most trouble. The others, he surmised, were probably asymptomatic. We discussed the surgery, but it cost $15 000. I couldn't afford that sort of money! We'd spent the best part of the last year on one income looking after Mum, and I'd only just started working full-time again. I was gutted. However, one thing led to another, and it was only a matter of days before I ended up back in hospital with another attack. In between bouts of pain, I explained to Dr Ventresca, a brilliant man by the way, what I'd discovered.

It was like my body was trying to give birth by forcing this thing out, but it was still attached at one side. My cervix had also been open the entire time. As my brain started to piece all these tiny pieces of information together, I decided on a plan of attack. I was going to get that operation come hell or high water. I wasn't going to let them take out my entire uterus. I would agree to them taking out only the offending tumour. While I was having a blood transfusion, to replace all the blood I had lost, a doctor came to me and said there was an opening available in the theatre schedule. He said if I was interested, they could get in there and get it out right then.

'Hell yes! Get me in there,' I said.

A very simple, ten-minute operation followed that apparently went very smoothly. The offending fibroid was twisted off, and I was good to go. In a matter of hours, the bleeding stopped altogether. I was so happy to have the surgery, and to know that I still had my all my bits.

When you have major surgery, such as a hysterectomy, it impacts on so many levels and so many operations are carried out, in my humble opinion, far too quickly. The impact when the muscles in your stomach are cut is major, from a sporting point of view. The impact a hysterectomy has on your hormones is significant. Hormones are so vital to your energy, mood and body function not to mention brain function. Then there are the other side effects of losing your uterus, not to mention the psychological impact.

Having this smaller operation, as an alternative, was just the ticket. For me, as farfetched as it may have seemed, it meant there was still hope of me having a child. Yes, there were other tumours in there, but for now I was okay. With all the research I'd done I had a strict plan of supplements and lifestyle changes to help balance out my hormones. There was a chance I could carry a child. For me, it's all about keeping chances alive, pretending things are better than they are and then making them better, and rolling the dice. As long as I have something to aim for and keep working towards, I am happy.

After the minor surgery, I was back into training, albeit at a much-reduced rate. Sometimes I would laugh to myself at just how much fitness I had lost since Mum's aneurysm and my journey. *Oh, how the mighty have fallen!* No more 200km races for me anytime soon. Now it was a mission just to run a few kilometres. But I was back moving and on the road to recovery, with a whole lot more knowledge to show for the journey and a better understanding of my entire health situation. I knew so much to help myself, Mum and my family moving forward. In every situation, there is always (and I mean always) a silver lining, a lesson learned, an experience worth having. They are usually not pleasant things to go through, but they do move us forward and keep us developing as people: as long as we adopt the attitude of finding the good in amongst the bad.

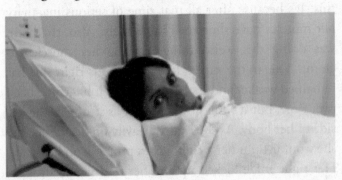

Yet another visit to hospital

Chapter Nineteen
Walking Backwards

It was now 2017 and over a year had passed. Mum was speaking in full sentences and her comprehension was building. She was beginning to walk further and further with less support. The next piece of the walking puzzle that we'd never considered was how to walk backwards. It is another thing that we take for granted and Mum just couldn't do it. Think about going to the toilet or sitting on the couch. To do these things you have to walk up to something, turn around, and then back onto it.

The other thing she couldn't do yet, which is vitally important in life, is to stop walking, bend, and pick something up. She still hates it when I ask her to do this. It's because after all that time of serious inactivity her muscles have shortened immensely. Also, the brain was doing this weird thing, causing her muscles to cramp. Due to the stroke, much of Mum's right side has remained weaker and less able. Some of it has come back over time, but it's still nowhere near as strong as the left side of her body. As she leaned heavily on her right side, she wouldn't put her weight down properly on her right. Her right ankle locked up and her foot would drop. It was a major problem as she was learning to walk, because her foot would drag along the ground, throwing her off balance and slowing her momentum. Her drop foot frustrated me because I saw it as hindering her recovery. So, I began researching cures.

I spent about $1 000 on a peroneal nerve stimulation device aimed at helping drop foot. It was sourced from China and worked by stimulating the peroneal nerve, which is on the outer side of your lower leg, responsible for lifting your foot. If you stimulate it, the foot literally lifts up. The idea was that it would stimulate the nerve and cure the drop foot. But it didn't work. Well it did on me, and it did on other people who had a properly functioning foot. But it didn't on Mum because the nerve was damaged, or the message was not getting through. We're still not sure exactly why it didn't work, and there went another grand.

There was also a device called a Vie light[17] that I bought for Mum. Vie light uses photo biomodulation. It's pretty complicated but basically it changes the cellular structures in the body, particularly cellular mitochondria. The visible infrared light is absorbed by mitochondria which leads to cellular repair and healing. It unclogs nitric oxide and recirculates it in the body. Nitric oxide is a molecule that helps to dilate the blood vessels and improve circulation. As it stimulates cells with light, it enhances the self-repair mechanisms in Mum's brain, and helps fix the damage caused by the aneurysm and stroke.

I spoke with a functional neurologist around the time that Mum was learning to walk. He explained that not

---

[17] Vielight: photobiomodulation therapy -www.vielight.com

only do stroke victims suffer issues with balance, but they can also have problems with their peripheral vision. He told me to research everything I could about the eyes and their impact on balance. So, I did. The discipline of functional neurology[18] is an extremely interesting one, and I was fascinated by what the eyes could tell us and how they could affect our brain function.

After a period of a couple of months of solid work with eye exercises, her balance really started to improve rapidly. Even though she's still not completely recovered, she falls over much less now than she used to. Later, we had her go through an eye test, and they confirmed that all the vision she lost after the aneurysm and stroke had now returned. It was awesome to hear something like that because to lose your sight would be so challenging. Her tests proved her peripheral vision that was lost had come back and that her balance was much better.

Out of all the weird and wonderful treatments, therapies and controversial ideas we tried, there were a few that I stuck with and maintained right throughout her recovery. I believe the hyperbaric oxygen therapy was one of the most profound influences on Mum's recovery. I ended up opening my own hyperbaric clinic with Jez, our sleep apnoea expert, and I was so disappointed with the lack of determination that people were going into rehabilitation with. They'd give up after five out of forty sessions, because they didn't see any immediate results. I'd beg them to keep at it, to keep pushing because it would pay off down the road, but they couldn't do it.

---

[18] Functional Neurology, *The Modern Brain*. Dr Titus Chiu http://drtituschiu. com/

Throughout this journey with Mum, we met many people along the way and shared our challenges and successes. One day, a man named Brian Hogan rang me and wanted to know all about hyperbaric oxygen therapy. I shared all the research I had done with him. Brian is one of the most determined and amazing fathers I have met. He and his wife have fought for their daughter who was severely injured in a car accident for years. The lengths this man had gone to were incredible, and I felt a kindred spirit in him and his fight.

Six years ago, Chloe was a fitness instructor in Auckland. On the day of her 22nd birthday, Chloe left for work in her green Mazda 2, affectionately known as Kermit. An hour later, there was a knock on her parents' door. Two policemen informed them that Chloe had been in a car accident and was in critical care in hospital. This was the beginning of a horrific journey that would consume the next four years of their lives. Chloe suffered a Traumatic Brain Injury (TBI). Over the next two months, Chloe would undergo procedures to place a probe into her brain to ensure there was no pressure build up, along with surgery on her broken arm, and a tracheotomy. She had a two month stay in the High Dependency Unit and during this time remained in a natural coma for twenty-three days. Her injury was similar to that of shaken baby syndrome. When Chloe was in a coma, a registrar at the unit spoke to her parents about the reality that she may never wake up and began to tell them of the option of removing life support. Two days later, Chloe woke up. However, Chloe was not out of the woods yet. Nearing the end of her time in the unit, she suffered two medical emergencies where her heart nearly came to a stop, and she had to be revived with a defibrillator.

It was with great relief that the family was able to see Chloe transferred to a specialist brain injury residential clinic after she stabilised. Chloe would spend the next eight months there receiving extensive physiotherapy, speech language therapy, and occupational therapy, along with general medical care for her injuries. Chloe slowly began recovering. Her sense of humour returned. During a shift change, a lovely older nurse asked her where she got the scar on her arm from. Without hesitation, Chloe told the nurse it was from a knife fight with al-Qaeda on her OE (overseas experience) in Egypt.

A year later, Chloe was released to be home with her family to continue her rehab. She had speech but was wheelchair bound. Like our journey with Mum they tried many treatments. They researched, talked with others and asked challenging questions of their doctors. And thank goodness they did. In one instance, a doctor suggested that they fuse both of Chloe's ankles so it would be easier for her to transfer from a wheelchair to the bed. When the family insisted that this would compromise her ability to walk, the doctor said, in front of Chloe, that there was no way she would ever walk again. Boy, did Chloe prove that doctor wrong!

It hasn't been easy or quick, but this family has thrown everything at her recovery. Along with a good diet and daily supplements, Chloe has been consistent in her rehab. The treatment they believe made the biggest impact was regular hyperbaric oxygen therapy. Chloe had multiple sessions for two to three weeks in a row at a private clinic in Mapua. They stuck with this therapy for just over two years. This is a huge financial and time investment, as they had to shift the family to Mapua for weeks at a time. I have just heard recently that this clinic is sadly closing its doors.

Chloe and her family found, like us, that many medical professionals know little about the benefits of HBOT and were resistant to include it as part of Chloe's rehab programme. However, over those two years, Chloe has improved in her cognitive development, balance, speech, bladder control, memory, and her ability to control her limbs has accelerated. Chloe can now read and remember books.

Late October 2018, Chloe competed in the Kawakawa Bay 5km Fun Run, using her walking frame for support. I have watched this young, tenacious woman fight her way back into life and love receiving her videos online and seeing where she is at. You can find a couple of Chloe's videos in the playlist. She is a fighter, as is her family. Our journeys have been very similar, and both have the same message: don't hand over complete control to the medical professionals and don't accept no for an answer and never ever give up.

Chloe and Mum's story shows that it takes total determination, a thirst for knowledge, an open mind and a relentless commitment to achieve the possible. Never give up, never lose the belief that a full recovery is achievable. Chloe continues to show the determination, toughness, and competitiveness that she has always had. Both Mum and Chloe are injured, but they are not disabled. Both will make a full recovery.

Sometimes, a journey to recovery is a long one. It requires persistence and consistency. It also requires goal setting and celebrating small wins. It's important to keep a record of your progress. Whether you are recovering from an illness or training, documenting your journey can have a hugely positive impact on your motivation and mindset. After Mum was out of ICU, I began filming and documenting her recovery. I didn't want to film her in ICU as it was just too horrific. But the little videos became a really important journal where we could see all the improvements over time. It helped us to keep us focused and on track.

In addition to the hours of exercise and functional movements, we also made sure Mum stuck to a strict, healthy diet supported by an array of supplements designed to enhance cognitive performance. In particular, I got heavily into researching nootropics[19], a new class of supplements and drugs that are all aimed at cognitive enhancement. I was also pedantic at keeping Mum hydrated. In my research, I came across studies where people were classed with having dementia but were actually severely dehydrated. When hydrated properly, they regained cognitive function. So many older people, especially, have cognitive difficulties just due to dehydration. Cups of tea just don't cut it.

Our multi-pronged systemic approach was really working for Mum. With the HBOT treatments, the TENS device, the vie light infrared light therapy, massage, the nootropic brain enhancing supplements, hair tissue mineral testing, functional neurology methods, speech therapy, the constant movement of us working her limbs

---

[19] Nootropics: Brain enhancing Supplements-https://nootropicsdepot.
com/ and https://
www.nootropics.com/

through the motions, a strict diet, and all the new wacky and wonderful theories, gadgets and gizmos I found on the internet, were starting to make a difference! It was never going to be one thing. All these in combination added up to success. No one thing is responsible for the achievements we made. Yes, I spent lots of money on things that I couldn't have accurately said they worked, but for me the key was that I was prepared to throw everything and anything at it. If I did the research and thought it was worth trying, and it wouldn't hurt her, I did it. I played doctor, and I couldn't honestly say that I didn't take risks, but I researched thoroughly and then made an educated call on things. I did my due diligence, ensuring I was making the most informed decision possible. Anytime a problem arose, we found a solution for it or tried to. Then it was onto the next problem, and so on until she improved. Some of the treatments sounded downright strange, but I looked into them nonetheless. If you always wait until the clinical trials are done, the thirty years of research are conducted and then hope that the pharmaceutical companies don't block it, or that there's money to roll it out, then you will be left waiting. I didn't have the luxury of time. Mum needed answers now.

One of the guiding principles I have in life is to never do things half-heartedly. I believe if you decide to do something you should do it to the best of your ability: give it 100%, no testing of the waters, no trying to see how it goes, because that attitude guarantees failure. I believe in going all in. Too many times people give up just before the breakthrough. So many times it's resilience and persistence that would have got them there if they just keep on going for it. Always behave as if what you are doing is guaranteed to work, with no ifs and buts, no hesitation and no second-guessing yourself. That is my motto.

We did the work and it paid off. Even to this day, we're all still there, day in day out with no chance of having a day off. We fight every single day for a little piece more, another milestone, the little wins. We take the knocks, and we try to remain focused and on task because this is my mother's life we're talking about.

People so often have a try of something and expect immediate results. They want to walk into the gym and walk out with the perfect body. They want the shortcuts and the easy way out. Too many are searching for the magic pill, the silver bullet that, in my opinion, doesn't usually exist. Unfortunately, some people aren't willing to put in the hard work and reap the real gains. Natural or alternative therapies, having a good diet, adequate hydration, exercise just don't work that way. They all take time and persistence. It makes me sad to think of all the people out there who were in a similar situation to Mum that could have recovered but didn't because they, or their family, didn't have the knowledge, the attitude, the ability to research, the patience and the determination to stick to it and keep pushing through the dark until they saw some light.

Although my pigheadedness can be irritating sometimes, it can also be one of my greatest strengths. Mum's rehabilitation was, and still is, hands down the hardest thing I have ever done in my life, and I have been through some tough crap in my life. Compared to what she had to endure however, it was nothing.

We recently spoke with one of the neurosurgeons who was involved in Mum's case. He said he'd never seen a recovery like ours. He said when they revisited her scans, four months after the initial aneurysm, that the aneurysm had shrunk and disappeared. He had no idea how it had happened and cancelled the second coiling operation that she was supposed to have. There was no longer a hole in her brain that needed plugging. He said, 'I don't know for sure if it was the hyperbaric oxygen therapy that did it, but something has fixed it, and I have never seen this before so keep doing what you are doing. It is working.'

Chapter Twenty
She Can't Float but She Can Drive

Oh my god, she can't float! This is not the thought you want when you've just helped your Mum into the pool. I watched her simply sink and flounder, unable to control her body at all. We were keen to get Mum back into aqua aerobics, which she had done religiously for over twenty years, three times a week. She loved the water. I hadn't been able to get her in there before now because she was just too weak to endure the temperature changes. Also, the ordeal of getting undressed and dressed was simply too tiring for her. Until now. I thought we could have a go, and boy, was I in for another rude awakening.

She'd been such a water bunny before the aneurysm. Mum loved swimming since childhood and used it to keep fit. But after the aneurysm and the stroke, she had no idea how to control anything in the water. She couldn't float, and she couldn't roll herself over onto her back like they teach children to do if they ever fall into the water. Mum was, as I would learn quickly, just totally terrified of the water now. She felt completely out of control. She knew she would drown in an instant if I let her go and that scared her. In fact, she couldn't even put her face in the water for a second, as she didn't even know how to shut off her breathing while her head was underwater. Once again, I hadn't even thought of this aspect of the brain injury, that these circuits that knew intuitively how to float and move would be totally broken.

Play List Link: See video on the playlist at lisatamati. com/playlist titled Isobel's First Swim

---

After that, we started taking her to the pool with a lifejacket on. She was quite terrified. Imagine the feeling of helplessness. I thought it would come back quickly, but it didn't, and it's still a journey.

For someone who has suffered severe brain damage, that's their new reality. They have to learn absolutely everything again. Mum's calf muscles, for instance. Mum really has no idea what to do with them. For you and I to take a step forward, we naturally roll forward off the balls of our feet and use our calf muscles to push forward. But she can't, due to both the lack of mobility now in her ankles. She simply doesn't get how to contract her calf muscles, to push off the ground with her heels and to create propulsion. There are, as I have learned, a hundred levels to proper walking, and Mum is still on the continuum somewhere. We try to do calf raises to strengthen and train her muscles but she simply can't do it yet. She looks at me doing the exercise, looks at her foot and can't figure out how to activate it.

Neil and I, are always looking at ways to train and strengthen her muscles. He is an expert at what he does and has been invaluable in giving me things to try. I'm not a physiotherapist, but I've been training myself and hundreds of athletes and this helps me see things. I look at Mum as she goes through a movement and think, *Why do you look so strange doing that? What are you doing that makes it so odd?* When I do this, I can have a sudden epiphany about what it is exactly that she is doing wrong. I break the movements down into single segments and see how each part affects the kinetic chain. I observe the knock-on effects and sometimes these sudden light bulb moments have given me an insight and helped me correct what she was doing wrong, but it can take me hundreds of hours of work before I can see it exactly.

Sadly, this is where most people get up to with rehabilitation. They hit this wall and just give up. I have to admit, it's difficult. How do you teach someone to use a muscle we take for granted or how to understand what their elbows are all about, for instance? Even now, every day when we go walking, she can only walk for around ten to fifteen steps at a time before some part of a bad habit will rear its head. She'll shorten her stride, not put enough weight on the left side, or her head drops down to look at her feet, her right arm stops moving and swinging, she slumps in the chest, or she forgets that her right leg should be placed in front of the leg and just drags it up to the left. I have to constantly coach her to improve her gait, little by little. It's arduous, maddening work that we have to repeat every single day.

Mum can now walk up to two kilometres, up through trails and up steps. She can go around 3km an hour so the progress is great. If I take her on a longer walk, Mum's brain fatigue makes her steps get progressively more difficult, and we have to stop more and more often. We'll stop at a bench, do some deep breathing, close our eyes and reset the brain, and then get going again. Everything is done on a conscious level, with her movements requiring concentration. Sometimes I push her too hard. The doctors kept telling me I couldn't push through brain fatigue, and they are right. However, after a short break often you can go further. I treated it like sprint training. You can't run 10km full pelt. But you can do intervals where you run as hard as you can, then stop and have a break, and then run hard as you can again. There might be pain, frustration and tears along the way, but later when you're talking about it, you will always just remember you made it.

In life, and any rehab journey, the end result is what counts. Sometimes the going might be glacially slow, but you have to keep pushing. To run an ultramarathon of any consequence, it's all about pacing yourself. Sometimes you run, sometimes you walk, sometimes you crawl and sometimes you break and go beyond your limits. As long as you are always moving towards the finish line, then it doesn't matter.

Mum recently set herself a challenge to bring some more purpose into her life, so that it's not all about the physical rehab all the time. I think there are a lot of things in today's world that are challenging for the older generation, things we just take for granted as being part of our daily lives. Take paying a bill for instance. Most systems have moved to a paperless, online system. Even using a television nowadays is very different. Everything has become digital, which is fine for so much of the population who have grown up with it or use it as part of their daily job. But what about the older generation? We decided Mum should attend the local polytechnic to learn computer skills.

I drove Mum to her course, and we were both really nervous. She's always been a social person and loves talking to people, but we knew it would be a huge step for her. I have to admit, I was nervous about leaving her there. It was like taking a five-year old to school. As I left, she sat there in her chair, following me with her eyes as I walked out the door. She looked slightly freaked out. So much of her confidence had taken a hit that even simple social interactions were scary to her, let alone learning to use a computer. I had to be strong, and I had to walk away. When I went back to pick her up, she was so excited because she had set up an account and sent one email. Before I could get a word in, she asked me, 'Can I come back again tomorrow?'

She felt empowered, and I could see her self-confidence coming back.

Nothing good ever comes from staying in your comfort zones, or so the saying goes. Finding a purpose higher than yourself propels you to greater achievements. I hate to think of Mum just being stuck at home, bored and unable to go anywhere, organise anything, or control her life. This aneurysm journey had taken away so much of her confidence and abilities that it really concerns me. I want to find a place in society for her where she can be of help to others because when you have that your self-esteem grows.

One day, Mum and I were down at the port about to go for a walk. She turns and says to me out of the blue, 'I want to drive the car again.'

Now at that point anyone and everyone would have said that was ridiculous. So, I took a deep breath and said, 'Right. Out you get. You are going to do it now.'

She can't even drive the mobility scooter straight or her electric wheelchair (the holes in the walls at home could attest to that) but ... if someone really wants something, you back them. You give them a chance. Mum got out and slowly she wobbled into the driver's seat. As soon as I had managed to safely buckle her in (a mission in itself), her face just lit up. She took the steering wheel and turned back to me and said, 'Really? Can I try?'

'Hell, yes! We are going to do it, Mum.'

She hadn't shown much emotion since the aneurysm, but now she was beaming from ear to ear. I realised I had to make this happen somehow. I didn't know how, but I knew it had to happen.

I knew how much it meant to her. She had always been a very independent woman, and her licence was a big part of that independence. I know when her licence was taken from her, it really destroyed her confidence. To everyone's horror, we started driving around a closed car park to start off with, where there weren't too many things around to hit. But my God! My heart was in my mouth the whole time. Sitting there, clutching at the seat with white knuckles, she slowly zigzagged across the car park. I don't know how she didn't hit anything.

It was then that I took a moment to look at Mum behind the wheel that I realised how much it meant to her. She was ecstatic and that was an emotion I hadn't seen for a while. Her face was so full of concentration. I could see how bright her face was, and her eyes spoke volumes. This was important. I could see what she was thinking. She was coming back. She was really going to get her life back. But to make this happen we really had to set another goal: she had to get her driver's licence.

My brothers kept saying, 'What the hell are you doing? She will never drive!'

I stuck with Mum's goal and told them, 'You just wait and see, you doubters.'

Mum was getting close to seventy-six. First, she had to pass a medical. In between our usual daily routine of oxygen therapy, exercises, walking, and now driving practice, we squeezed in a doctor visit. This was the doctor who had seen her just before the aneurysm. Dr Carmi, a wonderful man from Israel, had bent over backwards to help us over the years. On this day he came to get Mum from the waiting room and expected to see her wheelchair there. When Mum got up and walked into his office, he was shocked and amazed. He sort of hopped along in front of her, eyes bulging. He was astounded. He told us he'd never, in his entire career, seen someone come back from such a devastating injury, especially someone of Mum's age. He called it a one-in-a-million recovery. My chest swelled with pride, as I looked at Mum and reflected on everything we had been through. *The odds are there to be beaten.*

Mum had lost her peripheral vision, her ability to move, and of course any sort of reaction speed as a result of the aneurysm. We had to test all of those to prove she was safe to drive a car. As she moved through the tests, I think the doctor grew more surprised with each and every result. Mum scored pre-aneurysm levels on *all* the tests.

I explained everything we'd done to date, all the crazy, harebrained ideas that we tried, some that we stuck with and some that we never tried again. When the doctor exclaimed how impressed he was with her eyesight returning, I told him I believed the hyperbaric oxygen therapy and perhaps the functional neurology training had a large part to do with it. Of course, I'm allowed to say that because I'm not a scientist, nor am I a medical professional. Although I can't accurately prove it, I would surely bet my life on it. Or Mum's, for that matter. The doctor listened to what I said, and even though he couldn't be sure, he agreed that whatever we'd been doing for Mum's rehabilitation, we had to keep doing ... because it was working.

With the passing of all those medical tests came a host of surprises. Proving her cognitive abilities were at pre-aneurysm levels meant Mum was able to get back her power of attorney, and with it, the right to control her own life. The medical tests were just the first step. Next Mum had to actually pass her driving test, with an actual driving instructor. How scary at seventy-six!

Mum failed her first driving test. But she had a great attitude.

'Oh well,' she shrugged her shoulders, 'Let's go back and try again in another couple of weeks.'

I was in tears; Mum was just such a trooper. The second time around, Mum prepared with some driving lessons. I know! We damn well should have organised these the first time around. With being so close to the goal, we decided to pay for lessons. When Mum explained what she learned in her first sessions with the driving instructor, I knew it was a fabulous investment. Apparently, things have changed since I went for my license decades ago. It turns out that I wasn't perhaps the best instructor. After Mum completed the driving sessions, we practised for months and months. She was so determined to have that control back in her life and to feel like things were normal again.

Bravely, she booked in for a second test. Afterwards, when I spoke to her about it, she said it was scary putting herself back in that position. She felt like she was fifteen years old, sitting next to the instructor. She concentrated fiercely and put all the skills she had learned into her driving test. She passed with a score of 95%. Mum had her driver's licence!

She still has some issues with parallel parking (but honestly, who doesn't). We do have concerns about her getting out of the car. I worry that because she is a little slow, she could get hit opening the door. As she's concentrating so hard on getting out of the car, she may not notice what is going on around her enough. I think that spatial awareness will come as she progresses with her recovery. We're not quite there yet, and of course we're fighting age as well. But we make positive habits, and focus on the little, daily tasks that will help improve, just a little bit more towards her long term goals.

Just like she told me to do when I balked at the 2 250km run through New Zealand, all we have to do is focus on the first step, and then the next, and soon the rest of it will take care of itself. We've proven that. Who knows what the next goal is for Mum. Right now, we're enjoying the normal, daily things that mothers and daughters do together. The roles are beginning to switch back again. We have our Mum back.

Now mum is fully independent, has her own car and is often seen out and about, in town everyday. How far we have come!

Epilogue

While writing this book, my husband and I were on our own fertility journey. We desperately want to have a family. Although my health is much better, a normal pregnancy just didn't happen for us. By now, you can imagine that things like my age and my health weren't going to get in the way of us having a child. We threw almost everything we had at it. We researched, we worked on anything that we thought would help, we believed this would happen.

Originally, this final chapter was to be about the successes of surrogacy, translating what we learned with Mum to the battle with infertility. But fertility can be cruel. Sometimes, no matter how hard you try, or how much you want something, it just doesn't work out. That's life. But like everything, it's about the mindset you bring to challenges.

After a while we concluded that I wouldn't be able to carry a pregnancy. At 46, I had been successful in getting pregnant, but we had lost our first little one at twelve weeks. This was a devastating blow. We really wanted a family.

We were inspired by Toni Street's story in *Woman's Day*[20]. Toni's best friend, Sophie Braggins, had been a

---

[20] 'Meet Toni's Precious Boy Lachie' *Woman's Day* interviews Toni Street. 27 August, 2018

surrogate, and this allowed Toni and her husband to have a third child. As I read about Toni, I thought that this could be an option for us too. Thinking I would test the waters, I contacted the editor of *Woman's Day* and told them of our long and difficult fertility journey. I happened to mention in the article we were hoping to find a tummy mummy, a surrogate. I then posted the story on my social media page. One of my athletes that we train left a little comment on the post saying,

'I have a uterus free if you want it.'

I wrote back a personal message saying, 'Were you serious?'

Nicole said she saw that post and decided on the spot that, yes, she was definitely serious.

'Yep, I am.'

That night, when her husband Kane returned from a long day on the farm, she told him she had written back to me. His famous words were, 'Well, you have gone and done it now.' I was ecstatic, but I had another request. I had to make sure Nicole understood I needed not only her uterus but also her egg. I fully expected her to balk at that. That really is another ball game, but once again she surprised me by saying,

'Yeah, I expected that and that's no problem.'

Now Kane and Nicole are parents to two gorgeous little ones, Parker, three-years-old and Ahli, five. They are epitome of the perfect little kiwi family. They live on a farm out the back of Hawera where Kane is a share milker and Nicole a nurse.

The following week we went to meet them and immediately we felt that we were connected. They had similar values to us. We even found out we were related and from the same tribe as Nicole, and that Kane had gone to the same school we did. Everything seemed so perfect. At that meeting, Kane said to us the only thing is we need to work around our calving season,

'During that time, I can't have Nicole highly pregnant, but other than that we are good.'

Then he said, 'You better be ready as Nicole just needs to look at sperm and she gets pregnant.'

Brilliant!

To make sure we were doing things properly and not jumping into things, we made sure Nicole had medical tests, psychologist chats, and we researched the legal side of it. To my surprise, none of it was a real obstacle. Throughout the whole process, Nicole and my friendship grew, and we became like family to each other.

A few weeks later, Nicole rings and said, 'Get down here on Friday, as I am ovulating then.'

Wow, this was getting really real. We went down and did what we had to do. We didn't go through IVF; we did it all privately. Just a jar and syringe was all we needed. Just weeks later, Nicole rang and just said, 'You have to come meet my parents and get to know them.'

We popped around for coffee one evening to meet her parents. At the end of the hour, Nicole pulls out a shoebox. On the outside is written, 'My first running shoes.' When I opened it, there was a pair of booties and a positive pregnancy test. *Oh my god, really, really?* Tears all around and a ton of hugs. We were all pregnant! On our very first go we had been successful. This was rather a shock as Haisley and I had been trying personally, month after month, for over six years without success.

My heart was full! Sure, I was freaking out, too. Haisley and I were going to be parents, and I didn't quite know how I was going to make it work. But I think that all new parents feel like this. There's a mix of excitement and blind panic, as the due date grows closer. My family was so excited. This would be Mum and Dad's second grandchild.

For every appointment, Nicole, Haisley, and I watched our baby grow. I couldn't believe how well Nicole was going. She coped with the pregnancy so well. All the while, I was madly trying to prepare life for the arrival of a baby. In an effort to calm the nerves, we began to organise the baby's room. I tried to work out how I would fit work, Mum and a newborn into our lives.

We had the first scan at twelve weeks and all looked good. It became so real to see our little boy wriggling around inside her tummy. We proudly bought our scan photos home and hung them on the wall, really now getting into the new reality. Twelve weeks is when you can start telling people, twelve weeks is when you are probably going to be safe. Twelve weeks was when we had lost our first one, but Nicole was young and healthy. We carried on our way waiting for the twenty-week scan.

At twenty-two weeks we went in for our second scan and watched him on the screen, thinking everything was okay. Then, just days later, tragedy struck. Our little boy came early, too early. At twenty-three weeks our baby boy, Joseph Rei Tamati O'Leary, was born. We knew he wasn't going to survive, and we were devastated beyond belief. He lived for nearly two hours. He was the most beautiful little boy and our hearts are still broken.

The plan always was that this book would end with a chapter about the arrival of our baby, but not like this. It was going to be a hopeful next chapter of our lives, type ending. Instead, it has been the hardest experience imaginable. Nicole was so strong and her husband an absolute rock. My Haisley grew as a man, in the brief time we got to be parents. He stepped up and did everything he could to be a father to our little one. He bravely cut the cord, cradled him in our arms until his little heart stopped beating. He organised a wonderful funeral and looked after Nicole and me. In that room, four parents were grieving, not two. Three families came together to mourn. Our midwives, who have become trusted and close friends, were amazing. I found blessings in amongst the horror, and our little boy's life was not for nothing. He touched us, changed our perspective on life, and bought our families together as we bonded over this little soul. We are all family now, connected forever.

I worried about Nicole, and she worried about me, and that epitomises the character of both of us. I love her and Kane like a brother and sister, and that's what they are to me, now and forever. I felt a very vivid and strong guilt that I had put her through something so traumatising and devastating. *Did I push too hard? Did I cause all this pain? Am I not supposed to be a mother? Why did it need to be this hard? Why did my baby boy die?* Why...

A few weeks on now, I'm still unsure I have these answers. But what I can say for sure is that life happens. We aren't guaranteed anything. We can push and push and throw everything we have at something. With Mum, I did this. I threw everything I had at it, and we won.

But, by the same token, I had done the very same thing with our attempt to be parents, and we lost. Not only had I lost, but I had caused so much pain and suffering, and for a while I felt that heavy burden of guilt and pain.

But as I work through things now, I have decided I won't change. You cannot control the outcome of life. What you can control is your goals, your dreams and the action steps you take towards that goal. What actually happens doesn't lie in your hands, and to feel guilt, regret and pain will help no one. It may not turn out as we want. You can do everything in your power and still lose. However, I truly believe there are gifts to be found in the awful times in life.

I'm not sure what the future holds right now. Haisley and I would still like to be parents. At the time of writing we have had yet another tragedy, another miscarriage, this one at least early on in the pregnancy, we have now lost three babies. My heart aches for each of my angels, and they will forever be in my heart. For the moment, it is time to recover and grieve. There is some trauma we need to heal from. But this experience won't change who I am and my attitude toward life.

It's important to take the risks regardless. You have to be in to win, as they say. Even if things turn out disastrously, use strategies that work to grieve, dust yourself off and get back out there. You have to behave in life as if things will work out. Gathering support, doing the research, putting in the hard work consistently, and having a strong self-belief is the only way that people achieve great things. Whether things turn out like you think they will is almost beside the point. There's no point in doing things halfway: all or nothing. Be relentless!

Appendix A: Principles

Throughout this story there are some underlying attitudes and principles that really helped us stay focused and pushing towards our goals. I have prepared a free ebook on Goal Setting which you can down at goalsetting.lisatamati.com/goals

Make hard work a part of your life's philosophy

We have all heard the saying "work smarter, not harder." That is true to an extent, but I would suggest working smarter *and* harder are the real keys to success. No one ever becomes a master overnight on just talent alone. You can't just *want* to be a champion. The hard graft, the daily grind, the small rituals that take you— often in micro-increments—towards success requires a 100% commitment.

Dedicating yourself to long hours of work and sacrificing those easy pleasures in exchange for arduous training sessions or hours of research and reflection or academic study, or those mind-numbing repetitions required to perfect an instrument or movement pattern, are what it will take to succeed. As a great quote by Jerry Rice goes:

Today I will do what others won't, so tomorrow I can accomplish what others can't.

Make everyday a learning day

As humans, we're all programmed to learn from the day we're born, until we reach our twilight years. While arguably no one remembers their first baby steps, we all had to learn how to put one foot in front of the other and make it across the living room into Mum or Dad's proud arms.

Now, imagine you gave up on conquering those first few steps as a toddler. Can you imagine how you would have faced every other subsequent challenge that came your way? We all had to learn how to put one foot in front of the other.

Learning is a part of life. Those who embrace the often frustrating and time-consuming effort it takes to learn new habits, routines, or training methods are those who position themselves for long term success. Don't become complacent when it comes to your growth and development as an athlete, professional, or individual. In the case of brain damage and rewiring the brain, it can take literally thousands of hours, but it can be done. Neuroplasticity is real and happens until very late in life.

Always assume that there's more to something you've already mastered and look for ways to improve upon past achievements. This is what separates the champions from those who never reach their potential.

Be clear about motivation

From the early days of human evolution, our brains are wired to protect us. Primitive humans faced very real dangers. Survival was visceral: avoid the predator, find food, stay alive.

Modern human beings live in a far less physically dangerous environment. However, our brains are still wired in this fight or flight protective mode which kicks into gear: whether it be to avoid being knocked over by a bus, dealing with a career setback, or handling a social embarrassment. Our brain is built to protect us. That's where the all-too-familiar angst-ridden voice in our heads comes from. As intelligent and evolving creatures, we must apply reason and rationality to those unwelcome mental intrusions, especially when buying into them seems like the more convenient option.

When that voice starts to list all the reasons you shouldn't pursue a new journey in life, stop for a second and examine it. Pay attention to your thinking patterns and pre-empt negative thoughts with positive affirmations. Replace negative thoughts with rational and calm internal dialogue that addresses and disarms fears. You'll soon find the courage to stay the course.

But this has got to become a daily ritual. It's about controlling negativity every time it sneaks in and turning that thinking around as fast as possible, repeatedly. Our thought patterns are like a muscle, you have to work at them. Every time we think in a certain way, we ingrain that pattern more and more into our psyche. It wears in a well-trodden path in your brain. It becomes harder to change. At the beginning, you might be training a very weak muscle, but if you keep on it, you can rewire your thinking. Minds are like parachutes; they only work when they are open.

The same goes for the people you surround yourself with. People often don't want to see others succeed because if they do, then what does it say about them? Stay true to your motivations, keep that positive internal dialogue going and always remain honest with yourself. That long list of excuses will soon transform into positive reinforcements that give you that extra oomph when you need it the most. Surround yourself with people who are positive toward you and your goal. At all times possible, protect yourself from negative people, even when that negativity comes from a place of love or fear, for you.

Trust your gut!

Learn to trust yourself. The experts aren't always right. Do the research, do your due diligence, look outside the well-worn paths and find ways around obstacles. If I had accepted the prognosis for Mum, she wouldn't be where she is today. If I had listened to the experts who told me, after doing all the scientific testing on me, that I was totally unsuited to doing endurance events and was way below average in my abilities, I wouldn't have achieved what I did in the sporting world. Back yourself!

Be willing to get knocked down

Getting knocked down doesn't say much about you; it's how you get up that determines whether you will ultimately succeed. See setbacks as opportunities for your personal growth. Instead of looking at the first bump in the road as an excuse to turn around and head home, use it as an opportunity to inform your game plan and adjust your strategy.

I can tell you that if it weren't for the many setbacks I experienced throughout my personal life and career, I wouldn't be where I am today. In fact, I am thankful for those difficult and dark moments in my life, even when I don't necessarily want to repeat them. They helped me to really understand who I am, and what I am truly capable of. They helped hone a resilience that is key to winning.

Find the blessings in the shitty times. Take heed of the lessons that lie hidden in your setbacks to uncover where things went wrong, and then go back to the drawing board—don't just quit! Any star athlete or business leader will tell you that if it weren't for the failures they encountered they wouldn't be in the positions they are today.

People don't need to be comfortable. People (no matter what age) need goals, dreams, challenges, and emotional reasons to fights. Only when we are challenged are we growing, improving, and moving forward, and that is the realm where you will feel fulfilled.

Your Motivation-Understanding your why

What got you inspired to chase this dream? Why are you doing this? What will you achieve? What are the benefits—for your health, your mental wellbeing, your confidence, perhaps even for your loved ones? Think really hard about this.

We usually are capable of far more when the "Why" is bigger than yourself, if it is for someone or something else. Dig really deep when looking into your why. Ask yourself the why question four or five layers deep. Don't just take the first reason as the deeper reason. For example a client might say to me, 'I want to run to lose weight.' Okay, but why do you want to lose weight? 'So I can feel better about myself and look better.' But why do you want that? 'Because I want to be a good role model for my kids. Because I don't want to die early like my parents did.' The deeper you go into this line of questioning, the stronger you find your why. In your "Why" you will find sustained power to overcome the obstacles and any lack of motivation you might need to overcome. You'll find your "Why not?" In these deeper motivations you'll find reasons to fight and overcome the fear and the doubt. It is there. You'll also find the strength you will need to plough on through the middle section of the battle (the part where it always gets tough), to jump over any obstacle in your path and reach the finish line and conquer that big scary goal.

When you take on massive challenges, whether they are sporting, professional or personal, there's something magical that happens when you stand on the start line, no matter what the goal. You'll be surprised what resources you can pull out. You will be able to do things you could never do in regular training or your everyday life.

You never know how strong you are until being strong is the only choice you have—Bob Marley.

You will find reserves and strength you never knew existed, if you are just brave enough to start. When I stood on the start line of the longest run I had ever undertaken, the length of New Zealand, all 2 250km, I felt like the weight of this whole distance was squashing me. I couldn't breath and felt the panic rising as I suddenly realised there was now no way out. I had to go through this. I started crying and panicking, and in that moment, my wonderful Mum came over and wrapped her arms around me and gave me some of the best advice in the world. She told me, 'Stop looking at the end goal some 2 250km away, concentrate instead on getting started. Focus on the first twenty minutes, on warming your body up, on reaching the first 10km.'

She said to me, 'It's too daunting and frightening to look at the goal as a whole. Instead, break it down into tiny bite size pieces and eat it a chunk at a time. Never lift your gaze too far ahead when you are feeling overwhelmed. Just take that very next step.'

These wise words have seen me through the toughest and longest of endeavours. Breaking things down, pulling your focus in close.

Understand fear and learn to live with it.

Fear is natural. It's there to protect you, but it can often come at inopportune times, like when you need to keep yourself together. Stare that fear in the face and then decide to take action anyway. Often, by doing so, the big fear monster shrinks in size as you walk towards it. Fear arises whether there is a real threat (physical and immediate threat) or if it's just a figment of your imagination (like public speaking or going for a job interview). The more important the outcome is to you, the bigger the fear. Differentiate between real and immediate life-threatening fear, like a man chasing you with a gun, and the perceived fear, like the nervous tension of standing on stage and giving a speech. Your mind, your biochemistry, unfortunately, doesn't differentiate between these two. You need to explicitly, intentionally, put things into perspective for yourself. Is this fear response really necessary and can you control it through breathing, thought focusing, visualisation exercises, or other techniques to control your physiology?

Just take that very next step. If you aren't in imminent physical danger then stand up, feel the fear and go for it anyway. Every big achievement in life requires discipline, persistence, preparation, fortitude and flexibility. It will be worth it. You just need to take that first step. And then the next one. I am not saying it will be easy, but I am saying it will be worth it. You can listen to my episode on 'How to stop fear ruling your life'[21]

Visualise, be persistent and consistent!

Great leaders go into the future in their mind and see a vision of what could be that others don't see. They then come back to the now and keep their eye and mind on that future. They set about making it a reality. Step by step. They see a future that others can't envisage and hold onto that vision. They go into that future: feel it, see it, touch it, and integrate it into their being.

Manifest what you envision. When you set goals, your RAS filter will kick into gear and pull out bits of information. RAS stands for reticular activating system. It is referring to a bundle of nerves at our brainstem that filters out unnecessary information so that the important stuff gets through. Let's say you want to buy a red Mini

---

[21] Episode 105: Pushing the Limits podcast and blog: https://www. lisatamati.com/blog/post/41751/HOW-TO-STOP-FEAR-RULING-YOUR-LIFE/

Coupe. All of a sudden you become aware of all these Mini Coupes around. Because you have made this a goal or important, then your brain will focus you on this as you have set this as a target. Your brain knows this is important to you.

This is why goal setting is so important. If you want to run a marathon, you find yourself seeing runners, running magazines, posts, etc. In the flood of all the things you think about all day, your brain helps you piece together all the important things around you, which helps you to achieve your goals. Manifesting isn't an airy-fairy principle. It is the subconscious, your intuition and connections, coming together to give you insights, ways, possibilities and ideas to get to your goal.

Persistence and consistency—nothing will be achieved if you just dabble, have a go, give it a little try. You have to be all in. Keep going day in day out, and not just when you see progress, not just when you feel like it, but every minute of every day, work towards your goal. Become obsessed with whatever it is you are trying to achieve. When you become laser-focused you can achieve incredible things. When you allow distractions to come in and divert your attention, you lose that single focus power.

Behave as if you are guaranteed to succeed, that there is no doubt. Pretend things are better than they are and set about making them better than they are. Put on your armour when you go into battle. Mentally gird yourself up to fight and prepare your mind.

Fail

Resilience. You will fail, of that there is no doubt. There will be obstacles, there will be setbacks, but the most important factor in success is resilience. An ability to just keep going, one foot in front of the other and when you fall or fail, get back up and go again. Strength comes from struggle. The more resistance you overcome, the stronger you get. That's true in sport and in life.

It's okay to doubt, despair, cry, fall down, and feel at your wits end. But you aren't at your wits end, so get back up and take another step. As long as you have breath, fight. If you are breathing, you are still in the game. Keep fighting and believing. There is always a silver lining to every apparent storm cloud. You just have to find the learning in it or the gain. The most horrible experiences I have had have often led to the greatest breakthroughs, mindset shifts, and growth. Look for the positive and turn it into a positive as quickly as possible.

You have to understand, you are going up against the odds, and you have ignore the fear and doubt and do it anyway. Every single one of us has been through extreme odds. Believe you can beat the odds, beat the statistics. *Be the exception.*

Develop habits and rituals

Develop habits and rituals that will build a framework for success. You can't control the outcome or final goal, but you can control the action, the steps you take along the way. You can decide what you are going to do in the next twenty-four hours, the next forty-eight hours, the next seventy-two hours, and so on. Habits, done consistently, are the building blocks, the stairway to your goal. Have a willingness to grind it out. Either pay the price of discipline or the much heavier price of pain or regret later. If you are too lazy to do it now, you will regret it later when you no longer have the choice.

Think differently and do your research

Look outside the square and think differently than others. The breakthroughs that are happening on a daily basis in regards health science, research, therapies, medications, science, and technology is beyond what any human can grasp. Just taking a local doctor's opinion, who may not be up with the latest findings or possibilities, may limit your success. Everyone is down on what they are not up on. In other words, if you have never heard or learned about something, you will likely think its rubbish without having actually done your due diligence to see if there is something there. I was always willing to entertain new possible therapies, gadgets, technology, and training ideas, even if they hadn't had years of clinical studies. I don't have time to wait. Make your own calls on what is right for you and find experts who are up on the latest information. The world's knowledge is doubling every few years. It's moving ahead faster than ever in history. There may be an answer out there somewhere and someone who can help. Find them.

Avoid, with a vengeance, anyone who tells you can't. Find people who tell you "you can." You know the odds, you know the situation, the risks, etc., now get on with finding people who will help you.

Be willing to do it all when there are absolutely no guarantees of success. You can chuck everything at it and still fail. Be okay with that. Trust the process. If you plant a vegetable seed and then proceed to pull it out to look at it every few days to see if it's grown, you will kill it. You have to trust that the carrot will grow. You have to blindly trust the process and wait the allotted time before you pull it out to look. And if you do, you will be rewarded with the carrot in the end.

Age is not a barrier

Don't be ageist. Our society is ageist, in my opinion. Don't listen to society's imposed limitations of what you can do and when. Make your own rules up and follow only your own high expectations of yourself. Sixty is the new forty. We are now able to take our own health and longevity into our own hands. The knowledge is out there to slow down aging, to remain high functioning until late in life. Make it your goal to learn what you can to stay healthy and strong and function for longer. It takes money, it takes iron discipline, it takes constant learning, but we can influence our own futures.

Value rest and recovery

Understand your need to recover. Rest and recovery are key to continuing the battle and being strong. Even though we are strong and fighters, we know the importance of healing and recovering between battles. We respect our bodies and minds, push them hard, but respect and protect them as much as we can.

How do you support someone else?

So how do you support someone going through a challenge? You stand beside the person you are helping and believe in them. Imbue them with your strength through finding out what motivates them and then using that blatantly to get results. As a coach and an expert in what I do in running, for example, if I stand beside my athlete who is lacking self-belief, confidence and knowledge, I say to them: 'Look, I have done all this, and I see in you that special element that will get you there. I know you can do it and, therefore, it will happen. Here is how, here is the next step ... ' When I do that, invariably my client or athlete suddenly believes that too. They are emboldened to take the next step and to succeed. There is power in believing in others, showing them the way and holding their hand through the challenges. They don't need naysayers. They need people who tell them they can and who will help them get there. They need people in it for the long haul. My crews were like that, and they got me through the toughest of challenges. My Mum is like that. She helped me through life's toughest times and continues to do so. Her belief in me, helped me to believe in myself.

CATCH, OWN, REPLACE

This is a technique that I learned from mental toughness coach Chris Dorris[22].

It's all about upgrading your mental game on an ongoing basis. Using the little challenges of everyday life to improve the way you think and the way you perceive events and the way you control your biology.

Picture this—you are in traffic and suddenly someone cuts you off. Immediately your response is anger. You are pissed off and that happens within a split second. Immediately our amygdala kicks into gear. You show the guy your middle finger and would

---

[22] Episode 104: Pushing the Limits podcast: www.lisatamati.com/page/podcast

happily knock his block off, at least that is your immediate initial reaction.

Now I want you to stop and "catch" yourself in his behaviour. Recognise what is happening and use it as an opportunity to stop it in its tracks. Recognise that the stress hormones are kicking in and that your thoughts are possessed, as if by magic.

Now I want you to "own" this response. Tell yourself that it's not the guy that has pissed you off, that it's solely your responsibility to control your internal world. Tell yourself that you are acting like a rookie, like a chump letting your amygdala hijack your body. You are not pissed off at that guy; you are pissed off because of your own reactions to the situation. It's up to you to turn on your logical brain and own this reaction and stop it.

Now I want you to "replace" that response deliberately with a logical gracious attitude that is gratitude. Gratitude is one of the highest states we can must, alongside enthusiasm. Now in our example, I am telling myself how grateful I am for the roads that I get to drive on, for all the people who worked on them to give me the chance to do that. I tell myself that I have a life where I can afford a car to go wherever I want. I am grateful that I don't have to use a horse or run—as used to be the norm in past centuries—to get where I want to go. Immediately this state of gratitude will change the hormones flooding your system. You will stop the internal frustration and anger and, instead, replace it with love and gratitude. You avoid being a victim of the things that happen to you.

Chris Dorris has a great saying: *It ain't bad, it just is.* When we learn to see events as just that, not being bad or good but just existing, then we can control our responses and change our destiny. This is a powerful tool. I am not saying it will be easy to stop that anger. But if you practice, practice, practice (just like training reps at the gym) you will get mentally stronger and better at controlling the direction of your emotional responses. Ultimately living a happier more satisfied life.

Be relentless

Human beings are capable of far more than we think. Our spirit can be unbelievably strong, our will incredible, our fight powerful if we don't give up. The people I have encountered over my career running, who have overcome incredible odds and done amazing things, shows me we can do more than any of us think we can. I have seen, firsthand, blind people running across deserts. I have seen a man with one leg run across Death Valley. I have seen a seventy-five year old run through Niger and Death Valley. I have seen a woman who broke her back and was told she would never walk run 250km with a backpack across part of the Gobi desert. I have seen eighty-year old's with double hip replacements and heart problems run 100km. I have seen people carry children with cerebral palsy across the Moroccan Sahara for 250km. I have seen a woman with multiple sclerosis walk the desert on crutches, 250km, again and again. One of our own athletes, who also suffer from multiple sclerosis, ran a 330km race in New Zealand. A fifty-five year old grandmother in the Himalayas in a 222km race beat me. I have seen my friend with osteogenesis imperfecta yacht across the Cook Strait in New Zealand, solo. He also skied down a mountain, worked out daily in the gym, and fought for the things he wanted to experience. I have seen another friend, who was hit by a truck and paralysed, fight his way back. He then went on to do hand biking marathons, only to be hit again by a truck, and fight his way back again to health, without losing heart or courage. I have seen the miraculous, and I know the human spirit is stronger than what we can imagine.

What do all these people have in common? They have grit, determination, a fighting spirit that never gives up. They have self-belief, and an ability to go against the odds and come out winning. They are willing to endure pain, to suffer, and to overcome obstacles. They are disciplined and focused. They are winners. They are champions.

If any of these principles resonated with you, and you would like to develop your emotional resilience, your mental toughness and your ability to push through barriers, or even your leadership qualities, then check out my MINDSETU[23]. This is an online course, the purpose of which is to help you develop mental strength, resilience, and a "never quit" mindset. It helps you to get out of your own way, so you finally achieve success. It uses techniques that professional sportspeople use. It is not just for athletes. You'll learn how to control your physiology, and to develop daily rituals that you need to succeed in any area of your life. To delve deeper into some of these principles, I have written an ebook for you to download called "The Mindset of a Winner" at mindset.lisatamati.com, and if you are wanting to get

---

[23] Visit: Lisa Tamati courses: https://www.lisatamati.com/page/mindsetuniversity/

some ongoing support and to really create change in your life by developing more mental toughness, emotional resilience and a never quit mentality, then please visit https://www.lisatamati.com/page/mindsetuniversity/

Appendix B: Resources

Here is a list of resources by experts, scientists and doctors on the treatments used in this book or others worth exploring.

Experts

Dr Paul G. Harch (MD), Hyperbaric Oxygen Therapy
Author of *The Oxygen Revolution,* Dr Harch is the leading expert in HBOT. He has a few decades of clinical experience in emergency medicine and hyperbaric medicine. This book is important reading for anyone wanting to look into the benefits of HBOT therapy.

Link: https://hbot.com/

Epigentics Testing Program by Neil Wagstaff
The Epigenetic Program referenced in the book played a big part in Isobel's full return to health and there is a good reason why she responded so well to it. This Epigenetic Program is a tool that measures your genetic code and its expression, from which we can determine the optimal

environment that your body and mind require, to get out of your own way and achieve the things you want to in your life. By understanding your unique biology, you will have a system that gives you a greater awareness of how your brain operates, what stresses it, what makes it feel like 'you', as well as giving you direct insight into the main barriers and challenges that stop you moving forward and slow your health progress.

We measure your gene expression, and give advice based on what your body needs right now. When it comes to gene expression, we are all different. The program measures that difference and then provides exact advice on the best foods, exercises, and behaviours to support your body's preferred phenotype: its observable characteristics. Then, when your body changes, the program will adjust your advice based on your new current needs or gene expression. This was key for Isobel understanding herself, and game changing for Lisa's coaching approach with her Mum.

With her Epigenetic Program, Isobel now has the user manual for her body. She understands when to eat, what to eat, what type of exercise her body best responds to, and when is it best to exercise. She has discovered the social interactions that will energise her, and uncovered her natural gifts and talents again, on her journey back to health.

We worked with many experts while developing the program for Isobel, in particular, Dr Cam McDonald who is a world leading clinician in the application of genetics and epigenetics to enhance health, wellness and to prevent and reverse disease. He hits the nail on the head when he says, *"Personalised health will ensure that when people are treated, the treatment is designed specifically for them as an individual. Tailoring medications to eliminate side effects and maximise results, prescribing unique exercise, nutrition and lifestyle advice to meet the needs of the individual to speed the effects is what we need in order to truly optimise health."*

Learn more at https://www.lisatamati.com/page/epigenetics/

Gary Moller: Hair Tissue Mineral Analysis

Gary is an elite athlete, rehab specialist and Hair Tissue Mineral Analysis expert that I regard very highly. He helped me with my mum and also with my own health issues. I highly recommend him if you are dealing with health issues to contact Gary and get a HTMA test done.

Link: https://www.garymoller.com/

Ben Warren: Nutritionist

Ben Warren is one of New Zealand's leading nutritionists. He combines science and functional health testing to provide holistic health and nutrition advice, training and products. His Be Pure supplements were another key ingredient in Mum's health programme.

Link: www.bepure.co.nz

Dr Mark Hyman (MD), Broken Brain
This is one of the greatest resources out there on the brain, Dr Hyman has produced two documentary series on the *Broken Brain*. In these he brought together over seventy top specialists in different aspects of brain healing. Dr Hyman is the medical director at Cleveland Clinic's Center for Functional Medicine. He is also the founder of The Ultra Wellness Center and is a ten-time number one New York Times Bestselling author. I highly recommend people buy this series and use it as a resource.

Link: https://brokenbrain.com/

Dr Scott Sherr (MD), Hyperbaric Specialist
Dr Scott Sherr is a leading expert of hyperbaric oxygen medicine. We believe that this treatment was one of the most vital for Mum's recovery.

Link: https://www.northportwellnesscenter.com/practitioner/scott-sherr

Dr Bill Andrews (PhD), Anti-Ageing
Dr Bill Andrews is both a scientist and an athlete. He has spent his entire life trying to defeat the processes that cause us to age. His science is intriguing. He also happens to be a Nobel Prize-winning scientist.

Link: https://www.sierrasci.com/

Norman Doidge (MD), Brain Researcher

Author of *The Brain that Changes Itself*, Dr Norman Doidge is a psychiatrist, psychoanalyst, and researcher of the brain. He has also written the book, *The Brain's Way of Healing*.

Link: http://www.normandoidge.com/

Dr Jill Bolte Taylor (PhD), Author of the book *Stroke of Insight* and a TedX talk of the same title

Author of *My Stroke of Insight*, Dr Jill Bolte Taylor is on the New York Times bestselling list. A neuroanatomist who suffered a debilitating stroke herself and who shares her seven-year journey back from the point of view of a scientist who studies brains.

Link: http://mystrokeofinsight.com/

Dr Scott Thierl, Functional Neurology

Dr Scott Thierl (Chiropractic) presents a series of videos on insomnia, neurotransmitters, adrenal and thyroid optimisation, neuroendo immunology, early childhood brain development, and employee wellness.

Link: http://www.yourbestbrain.com/

Here is the You tube channel link to Dr Scott Thierl who has some great information on eye exercises and functional neurology https://www.youtube.com/channel/UCgpa2uIrqyKCT8nYLBAzdAw.

Dr Lindsey Berkson (Nutrition, Chiropractic), Hormone Scholar

Dr Lindsey Berkson specialises in hormone health and helps patients with severe gastroenterological issues to avoid surgery. She pulls her research from her large personal clinical experience and scientific research from decades of work as an integrative nutritionist, gastrointestinal and endocrine specialist.

Podcast: Best Health Radio

Link: https://drlindseyberkson.com/

Pushing the Limits Podcasts

Throughout this book there are references to researchers and leading experts which I have interviewed on my podcast: *Pushing the Limits*. Many of whom are mentioned above.

Link: https://www.lisatamati.com/page/podcast/

Below is a list of key interviews that you can listen to via the *Pushing the Limits* podcast. You can subscribe to the show on iTunes or your favourite podcast app at https://www.lisatamati.com/page/podcast/

Dr Bill Andrews: 'On the Science of Anti-Aging.' Episode 53.

Dr Cam McDonald and Angela Jenkins: 'The Future of Personalised Health'. Episode 36.

Dr Lindsey Berkson: 'Scientist Hormone Scholar, Author'. Episode 28.

Isobel Tamati: 'Back from the Brink of Death.' Episode 72.

Dr Lior Rauchberger: 'DNA Testing for personalised health.' Episode 41.

Ben Warren: 'Talks about eating for health and vitality.' Episode 39.

Chris Dorris: 'Tough Talks with Chris Dorris-Mental Toughness.' Episode 104.

Podcasts

Here is a list of podcasts that are worth listening to:

- Unstoppable by Kerwin Rae
- Smart Drug Smarts: Jessie Lawler
- Bulletproof Radio by Dave Asprey
- Dr Lindsey Berkson's Best Health Radio Show
- Let It In by Guy Lawrence
- JJ Virgin Lifestyle Show
- Decoding Superhuman by Boomer Anderson
- Broken Brain with Dhru Purohit

Scientists' work to study

Dr Michael Merzenich-https://www.brainhq.com

Dr Paul Bach-y-rita-Neuroscientist whose amazing research has contributed hugely to brain research.

Dr Mark Hyman-www.brokenbrain.com

Dr Edward Tobinick-Stroke Therapy-http://www.tobinick.com/

Books recommended

Asprey, Dave. (2017). *Headstrong: The Bulletproof Plan to Activate Untapped Brain Energy to Work Smarter and Think Faster-in Just Two Weeks.* HarperCollins.

Doidge, N. (2007). *The brain that changes itself: Stories of personal triumph from the frontiers of brain science.* New York: Viking.

Doidge, N. (2015). *The brain's way of healing: Remarkable discoveries and recoveries from the frontiers of neuroplasticity.* New York: Viking.

Harch, P. (2010). *The Oxygen Revolution.* Hatherleigh Press.

Lipton, Bruce. (2015). *The Biology of Belief: Unleashing the Power of Consciousness, Matter and Miracles.* London: Hay House.

Pert, Candace. (1999). *Molecules of Emotion.* Simon & Schuster.

Taylor, J. B. (2006). *My stroke of insight: A brain scientist's personal journey.* New York: Penguin.

Further Resources

Mum and I weren't alone on our journey and neither should you be. We all need mentors, coaches and guides; experts in their area to help us achieve our true potential and to optimise our recovery and health.

One of the major people who were there for me on this journey with Mum, was my coach and business partner, as well as Exercise & Health practitioner, Neil Wagstaff.

Prior to Mum's story, Neil had already saved my ultramarathon career at a time when I was burnt out, broken and facing the biggest races of my life. He taught me everything I needed to know about working with my body—not against it—and is always at the forefront of the latest teachings and scientific breakthroughs in the fields of fitness, health science and running. Not only did Neil save my career, but also my health; helping me reach my full potential as an athlete.

When Mum was hit with the horrific aneurysm, it was Neil who I turned to first for help. We had already worked together for a decade: firstly as coach and athlete, and later as business partners in our running and health coaching business "Running Hot".

We'd had the privilege of helping thousands of people on their health and fitness journeys, but realised that we needed to take our skills and knowledge to the next level to help Mum return to full health. The programs we now offer, reflect many of the teachings and therapies we applied on this journey together.

If you would like us to help you with any aspect of your health journey, or want to discuss any therapies discussed in this book, please contact us here: https://www.lisatamati.com/page/contact/ or email me and my team on support@lisatamati.com

MINDSETU

"Are you living the life you want to?

Are you full of good intentions, but fall short in confidently reaching your goals?
Do you find yourself saying "I Can't, it's too late", "I don't have time", "I'm not smart enough" or "I am too young or too old"?

Discover what it takes to have the success you desire in your life. Develop
mental strength, emotional resilience, leadership skills and a never quit mentality
helping you to reach your full potential and break free of those limiting beliefs.

My mission is to help you develop mental strength, resilience and a **'never quit'** mindset –
to get out of your own way so you
can finally achieve *that* success.
The excuses stop here.

MINDSETU
https://www.lisatamati.com/page/mindsetuniversity/

Now that you have read *Relentless*,
checkout Lisa's other best-selling books on her running
adventures. *Running Hot* and *Running to Extremes*.

You can purchase these directly from Lisa at https://
shop.lisatamati.com/collections/books